PREFACE

Adulteration of food stuffs is a very serious matter. It is affecting the whole society to an extent which may well be described as almost dangerous. Let us take an example of soft drinks. In August 2003, Centre for Science and Environment (CSE) claimed 12 major brands of soft drinks showing 15 to 87 times the EU permissible levels of four deadly pesticides which are known to cause illness from cancer to brain haemorrhage. The sample of soft drinks contained - DDT and metabolites, lindane, chlorophyrtos and metathin. The danger definitely lies in long-term exposure.

The main law governing food safety in India is the Prevention of Food Adulteration Act 1955 (PFA). Rule 65 of the PFA regulates pesticides in food. Yet another section defines the standards of non-alcoholic beverages. The awareness of public about food safety and hygienic standard in need, requires serious attention. Any quantum of laws, rules and regulations would not serve any purpose until and unless the laws are properly enforced and knowledge, education, and objectives about food safety and hygienic standards are properly understood.

The book aims to highlight the contents of the main provision of Prevention of Food Adulteration Rule, 1954. Attempt has been made to simplify the provisions of the Act as applicable to various food stuffs. The main objective of the book is to eradicate the anti-social evils and ensure purity of food and beverages sold to the public. Preventing food adulteration serves a very important role in securing citizen a minimum degree of purity in the articles of food and thereby protecting public health and prevent frauds on the consumer public.

The book is divided into three parts: **Part I** gives an introduction to Prevention of Adulteration of Food and Beverages. **Part II** explains the provisions of the laws relating to beverages (non-alcoholic and alcoholic), milk and milk-products, spices and condiments, fruit products, cereals, salt oil, fat, bakery products, starchy food, sweetening agents, *vanaspati*, vinegar, gelatin, sweets and confectionary, food colours, colouring matter, packing and labelling, flavouring agents, insecticides and pesticides, preservatives, poisonous metals and anti-oxidants. **Part III** concentrates on the provisions and regulations of sales, conditions of sales and licences, food poisoning, offences, warranty, punishments, role of Central Committee for Food Standards, Standards of quality of food, analysis of food, Public Analyst and Food Inspector and sampling, sealing, fasting and despatch.

The text is supported by examples, illustration, tables, figures, references, and index. Model examination questions and objective type, short type and descriptive type questions, as well as frequently asked questions along with their answers are also included for the benefits of students and readers.

In the preparation of text and writing of the book, a great deal of assistance and help was rendered by many laboratories, government offices, organisations, institutions, research centres, experts and individuals, I am really indebted to all of them. My special thanks to Shri Sanjay Jain, Director, Aman Publications and his staff for their continuing efforts to bring this publication in the present form.

JAGMOHAN NEGI

CONTENTS

Preface v

List of Tables ix

List of Figures xi

PART I

1. Prevention of Adulteration of Food and Beverages: An Introduction 3

PART II

2. Beverages: Non Alchoholic and Alcoholic 17
3. Milk and Milk Products 30
4. Tea and Coffee 46
5. Spices, Condiments and Pan Masala 50
6. Fruit Products 68
7. Cereals 74
8. Common Salt, Edible oils and Fats 87
9. Baking Powder and Strachy Foods 101
10. Sweetening Agents 104
11. Vanaspati, Vinegar and Geletin 109
12. Sweets and Confectionery 113
13. Food Colours 117

14. Colouring Matter, Packaging and Labelling 136

15. Flavouring Agents, Insecticides and Pesticides 152

16. Preservatives, Poisonous Metals and Anti-oxidants etc. 159

PART III

17. Prohibition and Regulation of Sales and Conditions for Sale and Licence 173

18. Food Poisoning, Offences, Warranty, Punishment and Allied Issues 188

19. Central Committee for Food Standards 215

20. Standards of Quality of Food 226

21. Analysis of Food: Public Analyst and Food Inspectors 230

22. Samples: Sealing, Fastening and Despatch 265

Model Questions for Examinations 274

(a) Objective Type Question 274
(b) Short Type Question 276
(c) Define Type Question 278
(d) Frequently asked Question with Answers 280

Index 282

LIST OF TABLES

3.1 Standard for Different Classes and Designation of Milk 33

3.2 Standard of Quality of Ghee in Different States 44

8.1 Period of validity, Percentage of Sodium Chloride and Soluble Matter 88

12.1 Requirements for Toffees 115

13.1 Requirements of Tartrazine 118

13.2 Requirement of Sunset Yellow 119

13.3 Requirements of Amaranth 120

13.4 Requirements of Erythrosine 121

13.5 Requirements of Indigo Carmine 122

13.6 Requirements of Ponceau 130

13.7 Requirements for Carmoisine 131

13.8 Requirements of Fast Red E 132

13.9 Requirement for Coal Tar Food Colour 134

14.1 Usable eating in Foods 138

15.1 Restriction on the use of Insecticide and Pesticides 153

16.1 Preservatives Restricated in Food Articales 161

16.2 Use of Poisonous Metals 164

19.1 Name of Central Food Laboratories and their specified areas 218

22.1 Quantity of Samples is to sent to the Public Analyst 271

LIST OF FIGURE

17.A Specimen of Form VI-B Declaration 178
18.A Specimen of a Cash Memo 202
18.B Specimen of Form VI-A Form of Warranty 205
18.C Specimen of Form VIII: Nomination of Persons by a Company 207
19.A Specimen Form I: Memorandum to the Director, Central Food Laboratory 220
19.B Specimen Form II: Certificate of Test or Analysis by the CFL 222
21.A Specimen Form III: Report of the Public Analyst 233
21.B Specimen of Form IV 251
21.C Specimen of Form IVA Bond of Surety 252
21.D Specimen of Form V 254
21.E Specimen of Form VI 255
22.A Memorandum of Public Analyst 268

PART I

CHAPTER 1

PREVENTION OF ADULTERATION OF FOOD AND BEVERAGES: An Introduction

Offences relating to food adulteration have far-reaching consequences on the entire community. The health of the entire nation including children, women and old and infirm persons is exposed to grave danger and it is a matter of vital importance which should engage the attention of all those who are concerned with the enforcement of this law. So the law relating to the prevention of food adulteration would be enforced with appropriate strictness so as to make it effective and achieve the object of its enactment.

Adulteration of food stuffs is a serious matter and it is affecting the whole society to an extent which may well be described almost dangerous. Yet in their anxiety to put down the evil the courts are not entitled to ignore the law and the basic principles of our criminal jurisprudence. It was for the department concerned to produce proper evidence; and reliance merely on the so-called confessional statement said to have been made by the accused when sample was taken from him only discloses laxity of attitude and indifference towards law on their part. This can hardly be considered satisfactory or justified.

The act and the rules do not infringe the guarantee of Article 14 or the guarantee of equality before the law or equal protection of the laws. The act deals with the regulation of a class of traders with a view to preventing the widespread malpractices and to control them. The classification made is founded on an intelligible differentia which has a rational relation to the object sought to be achieved.

A person cannot assert any fundamental right under Article 19(1) of the Constitution to carry on trade in adulterated foodstuffs.

The act does not infringe the guarantee under Article 20(3) of the constitution in the sense that it attributes conclusiveness to the certificate of the Director of Central Food Laboratory, because it does not compel the retail dealers charged with an offence to be a witness against himself. The standards set in Appendix B to the Rules are fixed arbitrarily but are fixed after consultation with the Committee for Food Standards.

While interpreting any section of the Act or the Rule of the Rules, the fact should not be lost sight of that the main aim behind this legislation was to cure the mischief of adulteration of food which was eating the vital fabrics of the health of the citizens. To ascertain the intention of the legislature, the provisions of the Act and the Rules have to be considered conjunctively and not in isolation. Any repugnancy or inconsistency has to be obviated for effectuating the legislative intention. Thus the rule of harmonious interpretation has to be applied.

It is trite that the social mission of Food laws should inform the interpretative process so that the legal blow may fall on every adulterator. Any narrow pedantic, literal and lexical construction likely to have loopholes for this dangerous criminal tribe to sneak out of the meshes of the law should be discouraged. The new criminal jurisprudence must depart from the old canons, which make indulgent presumptions and favoured constructions, benefiting the accused persons and defeating criminal statutes calculated to protect the public health and the nation's wealth.

The Prevention of Food Adulteration Act came into force with effect from 1st June 1955. According to Section 1 the act is called as the Prevention of Food Adulteration Act, 1955. It extends to whole of India.

OBJECTIVES

The main objectives of the act are:

1. To eradicate the anti-social evil and ensure purity of food sold to the public.
2. To act as a piece of consumer legislation to regulate to some extent the consumer supplier relations. The consumers demand enforcement of discipline
3. Among the producers of manufactures of food to ensure safety in the realm of food. The consumer's legitimate ignorance and his almost total dependence on the fairness and competence of those who supply his daily needs have made him a ready target for exploitation. The act is intended to protect the consumer against outright frauds.
4. Adulteration of food is a menace to the public health. The Act has been enacted with the aim of eradicating that anti-social evil and for ensuring purity in the articles of food.
5. Legislation for preventing food adulteration serves a very important role in securing to the citizens a minimum degree of purity in the articles of food and thereby protecting public health. It also serves to prevent fraud on the consumer public. The day welfare republic has naturally assumed great importance. Any indifferent attitude towards this social evil of fraudulently selling adulterated articles of food is difficult to countenance, for it affects the health of the whole nation including the children on whom depends the future of the country.

The officers enforcing anti-food adulteration measures are also expected to realize that on their discharge of the solemn duty imposed on them by the statute depends the health of the entire nation; and any lapse in vigilance on their part or in conscientious discharge of their duty is likely to affect the health of the whole society including their own children and this must ultimately react unfavorably on the health of the nation and the capacity for effectively safeguarding and defending his liberty.

6. To protect the society against unscrupulous and anti-social dealers. In order to protect the society against food adulteration and the hazards flowing there from, the act has made a provision for taking sample of food by the Food Inspector and to have it analysed by the Public Analyst. In order to find out whether the dealer carries on his business in a straight forward manner or has been doing so against the interests of the society endangering public health, it is necessary to analyse the sample of such food. While the aim of the act is to protect the society against such dealers, it is also at the same time the duty of the state to protect an honest dealer against an unscrupulous Food Inspector.

7. The main object of the act and the rules made thereunder are to ensure the purity of food and the maintenance of public health by eradicating the evil of adulteration of food. These objects are likely to be frustrated if the words "shall forthwith" in the aforesaid Rules are ascribed a narrow mandatory connotation in analyzing or sending the report and thereby would vitiate the trial that would enable many guilty persons of this social crime to go scot-free.

8. The Act has been enacted with the aim of eradicating the anti-social evil and for ensuring purity in the articles of food.

9. To ensure that the food which the public could buy was *inter alia* prepared, packed and stored under sanitary condition so as not to be injurious to the health of the people consuming it.

ADULTERATED ARTICLE OF FOOD

An article of food shall be deemed to be adulterated under the following circumstances:

(1) The article sold by a vendor is not of the nature, substance or quality demanded by the purchaser and is to his prejudice, or is not of the nature, substance or quality which it purports or is represented to be;

(2) The article contains any other substance which affect, or the article is so processed as to affect injuriously the nature, substance or quality thereof;

(3) Any inferior or cheaper substance has been substituted wholly or in part for the article so as to affect injuriously the nature, substance or quality thereof;

(4) Any constituent of the article has been wholly or in part abstracted so as to affect injuriously the nature, substance or quality thereof;

(5) The article had been prepared, packed or kept under insanitary conditions whereby it has become contaminated or injurious to health;

(6) The article consist wholly or in part of any filthy, putrid, rotten, decomposed or diseased animal or vegetable substance or a insect-infested or is otherwise unfit for human consumption;

(7) The article is obtained from a diseased animal;

(8) The article contains any poisonous or other ingredients which renders it injurious to health;

(9) The container of the article is composed, whether wholly or in part, of any poisonous or deleterious substance which renders its contents injurious to health;

(10) Any colouring matter other than that prescribed in respect thereof is present in the article, or if the amounts of the

prescribed colouring matter which is present in the article are not within the prescribed limits of variability;

(11) The article contains any prohibited preservative or permitted preservative in excess of the prescribed limits;

(12) The quality or purity of the article falls below the prescribed standard or its constituents are present in quantities not within the prescribed limits of variability, which renders it injurious to health;

(13) The quality or purity of the article falls below the prescribed standard or its constituents are present in quantities not within the prescribed limits of variability but which does not render it injurious to health:

Where the quality or purity of the article, being primary food, has fallen below the prescribed standards or its constituents are present in quantities not within the prescribed limits of variability in either case, solely due to natural causes and beyond the control of human agency, then such article shall not be deemed to be adulterated.

Where two or more articles of primary food are mixed together and the resultant article of food-

(a) is stored, sold or distributed under a name which denotes the ingredients thereof; and

(b) is not injurious to health,

then, such resultant article shall not be deemed to be adulterated:

DIRECTOR OF THE CENTRAL FOOD LABORATORY

The person appointed by the Central Government by notification in the Official Gazette as the Director of the Central Food Laboratory and includes any person appointed by the Central Government in the like manner to perform all or any of the functions of the Director:

No person, who has any financial interest in the manufacture, import or sale of any article of food shall be appointed to be a Director;

FOOD

Food includes article used as food or drink for human consumption other than drugs and water and includes-

(a) any article which ordinarily enters into, or is used in the composition or preparation of human food,

(b) any flavouring matter or condiments, and

(c) any other article which the Central Government may having regard to its use, nature, substance or quality, declare, by notification in the Official Gazette, as food for the purposes;

FOOD (HEALTH) AUTHORITY

The Director of Medical and Health Services or the Chief Officer in-charge of Health Administration in a State, by whatever designation he is known, and includes any officer empowered by the Central Government or the State Government, by notifications in the Official Gazette, to exercise the power and perform the duties of the Food (Health) Authority with respect to such local area as may be specified in the notification:

LOCAL AREA

Any area, whether urban or rural declared by the Central Government or the State Government by notification in the official gazette, to be a local area.

LOCAL AUTHORITY

(1) A local area is-

(a) a municipality, the municipal board or municipal corporation ,

(b) a cantonment, the cantonment authority;

(c) a notified area, the notified area committee;

(2) Any other local area, such authority as may be prescribed by the Central Government or the State Government;

LOCAL (HEALTH) AUTHORITY

In relation to a local area, Local (Health) Authority means the officer appointed by the Central Government or the State Government, to be in charge of Health administration in such area with such designation as may be specified therein.

MANUFACTURE

Any process incidental or ancillary to the manufacture of an article of food.

MISBRANDED ARTICLE OF FOOD

An article of food shall be deemed to be misbranded under the following cases:-

(a) It is an imitation of, or is a substitute for or resembles in a manner likely to deceive, another article of food under the name of which it is sold and is not plainly and conspicuously labeled so as to indicate its true character;

(b) It is falsely stated to be the product of any place or country;

(c) It is sold by a name which belongs to another article of food;

(d) It is so coloured, flavoured or coated, powdered or polished that the fact that the article is damaged is concealed or if the article is made to appear better or of greater value than it really is;

(e) False claims are made for it upon the label or otherwise;

(f) When sold in package which have been sealed or prepared by or at the instance of the manufacturer or producer and which bear his name and address, the contents of each package are not conspicuously and correctly stated on the outside thereof within the limits of variability prescribed;

(g) The package containing it, or the label on the package bears any statement, design or device regarding the ingredients or the substances contained therein, which is false or misleading in any material particular; or if the package is otherwise deceptive with respect to its contents;

(h) If the package containing it or the label on the package bears the name of a fictitious individual or company as the manufacturer or producer of the article;

(i) It purports to be, or is represented as being, for special dietary uses, unless its label bears such information as may be prescribed concerning its vitamin mineral or other dietary properties in order sufficiently to inform its purchaser as to its value for such uses;

(j) It contains any artificial flavouring, artificial colouring or chemical preservative, without a declaratory label stating that fact, or in contravention of the requirements of this Act or rules made thereunder;

(k) It is not labeled in accordance with the requirements of this Act or rules made thereunder;

PACKAGE

A package is box, bottle, casket, tin, barrel, case, receptacle, sack, bag, wrapper or other thing in which an article of food is placed or packed;

PREMISES

Premises include any shop, stall, or place where any article of food is sold or manufactured or stored for sale;

PRESCRIBED

Means prescribed by rules made under this Act:

PRIMARY ARTICLE OF FOOD

Any article of food, being a produce of agriculture or horticulture in its natural form is called primary food.

SALE OF FOOD

In grammatical variations and cognate expressions sale means the sale of any article of food, whether for cash or on credit or by way of exchange and whether by wholesale or retail, for human consumption or use, or for analysis, and includes an agreement for sale, an offer for sale, the exposing for sale or having in possession for sale of any such article, and includes also an attempt to sell any such article;

SAMPLE OF AN ARTICLE OF FOOD

A sample of any article of food taken under the provisions of this Act or any rules made thereunder is called a sample.

UNWHOLESOME AND NOXIOUS FOOD

The words "unwholesome" and "noxious" when used in relation to an article of food mean respectively that the article is harmful to health or repugnant to human use.

The definition of 'sale' is very wide and covers not merely sale for human consumption, but sale for analysis exposing for sale or hearing impossession for sale.

If on the same day and pause time various food inspectors lift sample for an article of food from the same container the seller does not connect various distinct and separate officers. There can not be more than one prosecution. The source reasoning curved apply where one samples are taking of can article of good from various containers. The offences will be the same.

The word 'sale' in Section 2(xiii) covers very kind manner and methods for sale. A real sale as well as 'embryonic' sale are sale for the purpose of the Act. The expression for human communication or case or for analysis in the context means 'whether by human consumption for any other purpose including analysis. The subject is to emphasize that whatever be purpose of the sale it is a sale for purpose of the act. A person selling an adulterated sample to a food inspector could invariably inform that it was not for human consumption and there by ensure himself against prosecution for selling adulterated food. If sale for analysis is an unqualified sale for the purpose of the Act there is no reason why other sale of the same article should not be sale for the purpose of the Act. To insist the article sold for analysis should have been offered for sale for human consumption would frustrate the very object of the Act. A person selling an adulterated sample to a Food Inspector could invariably inform him that it was not for human consumption.

The words of Section 2(xiii) are wide enough to cover a forced or a compulsory sale as much voluntary sale and a sale of sample to the Food Inspector for the purpose of analysis is covered by the definition.

The Act gives a special definition of "sale" in section 2(xiii) which specifically includes within its ambit a sale for analysis. A sale for analysis must be regarded as sale, even if the transaction contains an element of compulsion.

In a prosecution under the Act the essential requisite to be established is that the commodity alleged to be adulterated should be one intended for sale. It is found that an accused was merely taking the milk got from the buffalo, owned by his brother to his brother's hotel and it was not intended for sale as such, the accused cannot be guilty of an offence under the act even if the milk is proved to be adulterated. It may be that the quantity of milk that was given to the Sanitary Inspector on demand might amount to a sale, but what has to be really decided is whether the milk which the accused was taking was intended for sale. But the hotel keeper who sells such milk, though it is used for coffee might be guilty of an offence under the Act.

PART II

CHAPTER 2

BEVERAGES: Non Alcoholic and Alcoholic

CARBONATED WATER

Carbonated water means potable water impregnated with carbon dioxide under pressure and may contain any of the following singly or in combination:

Sugar,
Invert sugar,
saccharin not exceeding 100 p.p.m.
Fruits and vegetables extractives and emulsifying and stabilizing agents,
Carobean,
edible gums such as *guar,*
Licorice and its derivatives,

Liquid glucose,
Fructose,
Preservatives,
Permitted flavouring,
Colouring matter,
fumaric acid and sorbitol,
Arabic,
edible gelatin,
Gum ghatti,
Salts of sodium,
Calcium and Magnesium,

Dextrose monohydrate,
Honey,
Citric acid,
Tartaric acid,
Phosphoric acid,
Lactic acid,
Karaya,
Ascorbic acid malic acid,
Furcellaran, tragacanth,
Albumin,
Vitamins,
Caffeine not exceeding 200 parts per million,

and quinine salts not exceeding 100 parts per million (expressed as quinine sulphate):

Provided that in the case of sweetened carbonated waters other than tonic water and dry gingerable the percentage of total sugars expressed as sucrose shall not be less than five.

It shall conform to the following requirement, namely:-

(1) Total plate count per ml. Not more that 50

(2) Coliform count in 100 ml.

(3) Yeast and mould count per ml. not more than 2

Provided further that estergum used in carbonated water shall have the following standards, namely:-

"Glycerol esters of wood rosins commonly known as Estergum is hard yellow to pale amber coloured solid. It is a complex mixture of tri and diglycerol esters of rosin acids form wood rosin. It is produced by the esterification of pale wood rosin with food grade glycerol. It is composed of approximately 90 per cent resin acids and 10 per cent, neutrals (non-acidic compounds). The resin acid fraction is a complex mixture of isomeric diterpenoid monocarboxylic acids having the typical molecular formula of C20H3002 chiefly abietic acid. The substance is purified by steam stripping or by counter-current steam distillation.

Identification

Solubility

Insoluble in water, soluble in acetone and in Benzene.

Intra Red Spectrum

Obtain the infra-red spectrum of a thin film of the sample deposited on a potassium bromide plate-Scan between 600 and 4000 wave numbers. Compare with typical spectrum obtained from pure Estergum.

Test for absence of Tall Pass the test as given below:

Oil Rosin (Sulfur test)

When sulphur containing organic compounds are heated in the presence of sodium formate, the sulphur is converted to hydrogen sulphide which can readily be detected by the use of lead acetate paper. A positive test indicate the use of tall oil rosin instead of wood rosin.

Apparatus

Test Tube: Use of standard, 10×75 mm, heatresisant, glass test tube-Burner, Bunsen: A small size burner of the microflame type is preferred.

Reagents

Sodium Formate Solution: Dissolve 20g of reagent grade sodium formate, NaOOCH, in 100 ml of distilled water.

Lead Acetate

Test Paper-Commercially available from most chemical supply houses.

Procedure-Weight 40-50 mg of sample into a test tube add 1-2 drops of sodium formate solution. Place a strip of lead acetate test paper over the mouth of the test tube. Heat the tube in the burner flame until fumes are formed that contact the test paper. Continue heating for 2-5 minutes. There must be no formation of a black spot of lead sulphide indicating the presence of sulphur containing compounds. Detection Limit: 50 mg/kg sulphur.

Drop softening point	:	Between 88 degree C and 96 degree C
Arsenic	:	Not more than 3 ppm.
Lead	:	Not more than 10 ppm.
Heavy metals (as lead)	:	Note more than 40 ppm.
Acid value	:	Between 3 and 9
Hydroxyl number	:	Between 15 and 45

MINERAL WATER

1. Mineral water means includes all kinds of Mineral Water or Natural mineral water by whatever name it is called and sold.

2. **Description and Types of Mineral water:**

(1) Natural mineral water is water clearly distinguished from ordinary drinking water because –

(2) It is characterized by its content of certain mineral salts and their relative proportions and the presence of trace elements or of other constituents,

(3) It is obtained directly from natural or drilled sources from underground water bearing strata and from Public water supply for which all possible precautions should be taken within the protected perimeters to avoid any pollution of, or external influence on, the chemical and physical qualities and natural mineral water.

(4) Of the constancy of its composition and the stability of its discharge and its temperature, due account being taken of the cycles of minor natural fluctuations;

(5) It is collected under conditions which guarantee the original micro-biological purity and chemical composition of essential components;

(6) It is packages close to the point of emergence of the source with particular hygienic precautions;

(7) It is not subjected to any treatment other than those permitted by this standard;

(8) Naturally Carbonated Natural Mineral Water – A naturally carbonated natural mineral water is a natural mineral water which, after possible treatment as given hereunder and re-incorporation of gas from the same source and after packaging, taking into consideration usual technical tolerance, has the same content of carbondioxide spontaneously and visibly given off under normal conditions of temperature and pressure.

(9) Non-Carbonated Natural Mineral Water – A non-carbonated natural mineral water is a natural mineral water which, after possible treatment as given hereunder and after packaging taking into consideration usual technical tolerance, does not contain free carbon dioxide in excess of the amount necessary to keep the hydrogen carbonate salts present in the water dissolved.

(10) Decarbonated Natural Mineral Water – A decarbonated natural mineral is a natural mineral water which, after possible treatment as given hereunder and after packaging, has less carbon dioxide content than that at emergence and does not visibly and spontaneously give of carbon dioxide under normal conditions of temperature and pressure.

(11) Natural mineral Water Fortified with Carbon Dioxide from the Source – A natural mineral water fortified with carbon dioxide from the source is natural mineral water which, after possible treatment as given hereunder and after packaging, has more carbon dioxide content than that at emergence.

(12) Carbonated Natural Mineral Water – A carbonated natural mineral water is a natural mineral water which, after possible treatment as given hereunder and after packaging, has been made effervescent by the addition of carbon dioxide from another origin.

3. **Treatment and handling** – Treatment permitted include separation from unstable constituents, such as compounds containing iron, manganese, sulphur or arsenic, by decantation and/or filtration, if necessary, accelerated by previous aeration.

The treatment provided may only be carried out on condition that the mineral content of the water is not modified in its essential constituents, which give the water its properties.

The transport of natural mineral waters in bulk containers for packaging or for any other process before packaging is prohibited. Natural Mineral water shall be packaged in clean and sterile containers.

The source or the point of emergence shall be protected against risks of pollution.

The installation intended for the production of natural mineral waters shall be such as to exclude any possibility of contamination. For this purpose, and in particular-

(1) the installations for collection, the pipes and the reservoirs shall be made from materials suited to the water and in such a way as to prevent the introduction of foreign substances into the water,

(2) the equipment and its use for production, especially installations for washing and packaging, shall meet hygienic requirements,

(3) if, during production it is found that the water is polluted, the producer shall stop all operations until the cause of pollution is eliminated'

4. All Minieral water shall conform to the following standards, namely:-

S.No.	Characteristic		Requirements
1.	Colour, Hazan Unit/ True Colour Unit	:	Not more than 2
2.	Odour	:	Agreeable
3.	Taste	:	Agreeable
4.	Turbidity	:	Not more than 2 nephelometric turbidity unit (NTU)
5.	Total Dissolved solids	:	150-700 mg/litre
6.	PH	:	6.5-8.5

7. Nitrates (as NO_3)	: Not more than 50 mg/litre
8. Nitrites (as NO_2)	: Not more than 0.02 mg/litre
9. Sulphide (as H_2S)	: Not more than 0.05 mg/litre
10. Mineral Oil	: Not detectable
11. Phenolic compounds (as C_6H_5OH)	: Not detectable
12. Manganese (as Mn)	: Not more than 2.0 mg/litre
13. Copper (as CU)	: Not more than 1 mg/litre
14. Zinc (as CU)	: Not more than 5 mg/litre
15. Fluoride (as F)	: Not more than 1 mg/litre
16. Barium (as Ba)	: Not more than 1.0 mg/litre
17. Antimony (as Sb)	: Not more than 0.005 mg/litre
18. Nickel (as Ni)	: Not more than 0.02 mg/litre
19. Borate (as B)	: Not more than 5 mg/litre
20. Surface active agents	: Not dectable
21. Silver (as Ag)	: Not more than 0.01 mg/litre
22. Chlorides (as Cl)	: Not more than 200 mg/litre
23. Sulphate (as SO_4)	: Not more than 200 mg/litre
24. Magnesium (as Mg)	: Not more than 50 mg/litre
25. Calcium (as Ca)	: Not more than 100 mg/litre
26. Sodium (a Na)	: Not more than 150 mg/litre
27. Alkalinity (as HCO_3)	: 75-400 mg/litre
28. Arsenic (as As)	: Not more than 0.05 mg/litre
29. Cadmium (as Cd)	: Not more than 0.003 mg/litre
30. Cyanide (as CN)	: Not more than 0.07 mg/litre
31. Chromium (as Cr)	: Not more than 0.05 mg/litre

32. Mercury (as Hg)	:	Not more than 0.001 mg /litre
33. Lead (as Pb)	:	Not more than 0.01 mg/litre
34. Selenium (as Se)	:	Not more than 0.05 mg/litre
35. Poly nuclear aromatic Hydrocarbons	:	Not detectable
36. Polychlorinated biphenyle (PCB)	:	Not detectable
37. Pesticide Residue	:	Below detectable limits
38. "Alpha" activity	:	Not more than 0.1 Bacqueral/ litre (Bq)
39. "Beta" activity	:	Not more than 1 pico curie/ litre (pCi)
40. Yeast and mould counts	:	Absent
41. Salmonella and Shigella	:	Absent
42. E. Coil or thermotolerant Coliforms 1 × 250 ml	:	Absent
43. Total coliform bacteria A × 250 ml	:	Absent
44. Facal Streptoocci and Staphylococcus Aureus 1 × 250 ml	:	Absent
45. Pseudomonas aeruginosa 1 × 250 ml	:	Absent
46. Sulphite-reducing anaerobes 1 × 50 ml	:	Absent
47. Vibrocholera 1 × 250 ml	:	Absent
48. V Parahaemolyticus 1 × 250 ml	:	Absent

Labelling Prohibitions

No claims concerning medicinal (preventative, alleviative or curative) effects shall be made in respect of the properties of the product covered by the standard. Claims of other beneficial effects related to the health of the consumer shall not be made.

The name of the locality, hamlet or specified place may not form part of the trade name unless it refers to a natural mineral water collected at the place designated by that trade name.

The use of any statement or of any pictorial device which may create confusion in the mind of the public or in any way mislead the public about the nature, origin, composition and properties or natural mineral water put on sale is prohibited.

PACKAGED DRINKING WATER (OTHER THAN MINERAL WATER)

"Packaged drinking water" means water derived from any source of potable water which is subjected to treatments, namely, decanatation, filter, depth filter, cartidge filer, activated carbon filteration, demineralisation, remineralisation reverse ormosis and packed. It may be disinfected by means of chemical agents and/ or physical method of the number of micro-organism to a level that does not compromise food safety or suitability.

It shall be packed in clean, sterile, colourless, transparent and tamperproof bottles/containers made of polyethlene (PE) conforming to IS: 10146 or polyvinyl chloride (PVC) conforming to IS:12252 or polypropylene conforming to IS: 10910 or foodgrade polycarbonate or sterile glass bottles suitable for preventing possible aulteration or contamination of the water. .

All packaging materials of plastic origin shall pass the overall migration and colour migration limits as laid down in the relevant Indian Standards for products for respective packaging materials.

It shall confrom to the following standards namely:-

S.No.	Characteristic		Requirements
1.	Colour	:	Not more than 2 Hazen units/ True Colour units
2.	Odour	:	Agreeable
3.	Taste	:	Agreeable
4.	Turbidity	:	Not more than 2 nephelometric turbidity unit (NTU)
5.	Total Dissolved solids	:	Not more than 500 mg/litre
6.	PH	:	6.5-8.5
7.	Nitrates (as NO_3)	:	Not more than 45 mg/litre
8.	Nitrites (as NO_2)	:	Not more than 0.02 mg/litre
9.	Sulphide (as H_2S)	:	Not more than 0.05 mg/litre
10.	Mineral Oil	:	Not more than 0.01 mg/litre
11.	Phenolic compounds (as C_6H_5OH)	:	Not more than 0.01 mg/litre
12.	Manganese (as Mn)	:	Not more than 0.5 mg/litre
13.	Copper (as CU)	:	Not more than 1 mg/litre
14.	Zinc (as CU)	:	Not more than 5 mg/litre
15.	Fluoride (as F)	:	Not more than 1.0 mg/litre
16.	Barium (as Ba)	:	Not more than 1.0 mg/litre
17.	Antimony (as Sb)	:	Not more than 0.005 mg/litre
18.	Nickel (as Ni)	:	Not more than 0.02 mg/litre
19.	Borate (as B)	:	Not more than 5 mg/litre
20.	Anionic surface active agents (as MBAS)	:	Not more than 0.2 mg/litre
21.	Silver (as Ag)	:	Not more than 0.01 mg/litre

22. Chlorides (as Cl)	: Not more than 200 mg/litre
23. Sulphate (as SO_4)	: Not more than 200 mg/litre
24. Magnesium (as Mg)	: Not more than 30 mg/litre
25. Calcium (as Ca)	: Not more than 75 mg/litre
26. Sodium (a Na)	: Not more than 200 mg/litre
27. Alkalinity (as HCO_3)	: Not more than 200 mg/litre
28. Arsenic (as As)	: Not more than 0.05 mg/litre
29. Cadmium (as Cd)	: Not more than 0.01 mg/litre
30. Cyanide (as CN)	: Not more than 0.05 mg/litre
31. Chromium (as Cr)	: Not more than 0.05 mg/litre
32. Mercury (as Hg)	: Not more than 0.001 mg /litre
33. Lead (as Pb)	: Not more than 0.01 mg/litre
34. Selenium (as Se)	: Not more than 0.01 mg/litre
35. Poly nuclear aromatic Hydrocarbons	: Not detectable
36. Polychlorinated biphenyle (PCB)	: Not detectable
37. Aluminium (as Al)	: Not more than 0.03 mg/litre
38. Residual free chlorine	: Not more than 0.2 mg/litre
39. Pesticide Residue	: Below detectable limits
40. "Alpha" activity	: Not more than 0.1 Bacqueral/ litre (Bq)
41. "Beta" activity	: Not more than 1 pico curie/ litre (pCi)
42. Yeast and mould counts	: Absent
43. Salmonella and Shigella	: Absent
44. E. Coil or thermotolerant Coliforms 1 × 250 ml	: Absent

45. Total coliform bacteria A × 250 ml	:	Absent
46. Facal Streptoocci and Staphylococcus Aureus 1 × 250 ml	:	Absent
47. Pseudomonas aeruginosa 1 × 250 ml	:	Absent
48. Sulphite-reducing anaerobes 1 × 50 ml	:	Absent
49. Vibrocholera 1 × 250 ml	:	Absent
50. V Parahaemolyticus 1 × 250 ml	:	Absent
51. Aerobic Microbial Count	:	The total viable colony count shall not exceed 100 per ml at 20 degree C. to 22 degree C in 72 h or agar – agar or on agar – gelatin mixture, and 20 per ml at 37 degree C in 24 h on agar-agar.

Labelling Prohibitions

No claims concerning medicinal (preventative, alleviative or curative) effects shall be made in respect of the properties of the product covered by the standard. Claims of other beneficial effects related to the health of the consumer shall not made.

The name of the locality, hamlet or specified place may not form part of the trade name unless it refers to packaged mineral water collected at the place designated by that trade name.

The use of any statement or of any pictorial device which may create confusion in the mind of the public or in any way mislead the public about the nature, origin, composition and properties of such waters put on sale is prohibited.

Note—Without prejudice to the standards laid down in this Appendix, whenever water is used in the manufacture or preparation of any article or food, such water shall be free from micro-organism likely to cause disease and also free from chemical constituents which may impair health.

BEVERAGES ALCOHOLIC

TODAY

Today means the sap from coconut, date, today palm tree or any other kind of palm tree which has undergone alcoholic fermentation. It shall be white cloudy in appearance which sediments on storage and shall possess characteristic flavour derived from the sap and fermentation without addition of extraneous alcohol. It shall be free from added colouring matter, dirt, other foreign matter or any other ingredient injurious to health. It shall also be free from chloral hydrate, paraldehyde, sedative tranquilizer and artificial sweetner.

It shall also conform to the following standards, namely:-

(a) Alcoholic content – Not less than 5 percent (v/v).

(b) Total acid as tartaric acid (expressed in terms of 100 lt. of absolute alcohol) Not more than 400 grams.

(c) Volatile acid as acetic acids (expressed in terms of 100 litres of abosulute alcohol) Not more than 100 grams.

CHAPTER 3

MILK AND MILK PRODUCTS

MILK

The secretion derived from complete milking of healthy much animals. It shall be free from colostrums. Milk of different classes and of different designations shall conform to the standards laid in Table 3.1.

PASTEURIZATION

The term pasteurization, when used in association with milk and milk products, means heating milk / milk product by a heat treatment as mentioned below and cooling to a suitable temperature before distribution. Pasteurized milk/milk product shall show a negative Phosphatase Test.

The term "Pasteurization", "Pasteurized" and similar terms shall be taken to refer to the process of heating every particle of milk or milk product to at least 63°C, and holding at such temperature continuously for at least 30 minutes, or heating it to at least 71.5°C, and holding at such temperature continuously for at least 15 seconds or an approved temperature-time combination that will serve to give a negative Phosphatase Test.

All pasteurized milk and milk products shall be cooled immediately to a temperature of 10°C, or less, and shall be maintained thereat until delivery.

The term silk product, in context to A.11.01.02, means standardized milk, recombined milk, toned milk, double toned milk, skimmed milk and flavoured milk.

STERILIZATION

The term sterilization, when used in association with milk means heating milk continuously to a temperature of 115°C for 15 minutes or 145°C for 3 seconds, or equivalent approved temperature, time combination to ensure preservation at room temperature for a period of not less than 15 days from the date of manufacture. Sterilized milk shall show absence of albumen by a negative Turbidity Test. Sterilized milk shall be sold only in the container in which the milk was sterilized.

BOILED MILK

Milk which has been brought to boil.

FLAVOURED MILK

By whatever name called, may contain nuts (whole, fragmented or ground) chocolate, coffee or any other edible food colours and cane sugar. Flavoured milk shall be pasteurized, sterilized or boiled. The type of milk shall be mentioned on the label.

MIXED MILK

A combination of milk of cow, buffalo, sheep, goat or any other milch animal and maybe a combination of any of these milk which has been made and conforms to the standards given in Table 3.1.

STANDARDISED MILK

Cow milk or buffalo milk or sheep milk or goat milk or a combination of any of these milk that has been standardized to a fat percentage given in Table 3.1 the abstraction and/or addition of milk of fat, or by the addition of skimmed milk or by addition of recombined or reconstituted skimmed milk,

Standardised milk shall be pasteurized and shall show a negative Phosphatase Test.

RECOMBINED MILK

The homogenized product prepared from milk fat, non-fat-milk solids and water. Recombined milk shall be pasteurized and shall show a negative Phosphatase Test.

TONED MILK

The product prepared by admixture of cow or buffalo milk or both with fresh skimmed milk; or by admixture of cow or buffalo milk or both with non-fat-milk solids or milk powder and water; or by partial abstraction/addition of fat from/to milk. It shall be pasteurized and shall show a negative Phosphatase Test. When fat or dry non-fat-milk solids are used, it shall be ensured that the product remains homogeneous and no deposition of solids takes places on standing.

DOUBLE TONED MILK

The product prepared by admixture of cow or buffalo milk or both with fresh skimmed milk, or by admixture of cow or buffalo milk or both with non-fat milk solids and water, or by partial abstraction/addition of fat from/to milk. It shall be pasteurized and shall show a negative phosphatase Test. When fat or dry non fat-milk solids are used, it shall be ensured that the product remains homogeneous and no deposition of solids takes place on standing.

SKIMMED MILK

The product prepared from milk from which almost all the milk fat has been removed mechanically.

Standards for different classes and designations of milk shall be given Table 3.1.

Table 3.1: Standard for Different Classes and Designation of Milk

Class of Milk	Designation	Locality	Minimum per cent	
			Milk fat	Milk solids non-fat
Buffalo Milk	Raw, Pasteurized, Boiled, flavoured and Sterilized.	Assam Bihar Chandigarh Delhi Gujarat Haryana Jharkhand Maharashtra Punjab Uttaranachal Uttar Pradesh West Bengal	6.0	9.0
		Andaman & Nicobar Andhra Pradesh Dadra & Nagar Haveli Goa, Daman & Diu Kerala Laccadive, Minicoy & A. Islands Madras Madhya Pradesh Chhatisgargh Manipur Mysore Nagaland NEFA Orissa Pondicherry Rajasthan Tripura	5.0	9.0
Cow Milk	Raw, Pasteurized, Boiled, Flavoured and Sterilized	Chandigarh Haryana Punjab	4.0	8.5
		Andaman & Nicobar Andhra Pradesh Assam Bihar and Jharkhand Dadara & Nagar Haveli Delhi		

(contd)

Class of Milk	Designation	Locality	Minimum per cent	
			Milk fat	Milk solids non-fat
		Goa, Daman & Diu		
		Gujarat		
		Himachal Pradesh		
		Kerala		
		Laccadive, Minicoy & A. Islands		
		Madhya Pradesh	3.5	8.5
		Chhatisgargh		
		Madras		
		Maharashtra		
		Manipur		
		Mysore		
		Nagaland		
		NEFA		
		Pondicherry		
		Rajasthan		
		Tripura		
		Uttaranchal		
		Uttar Pradesh	3.0	8.5
		West Bengal		
		Orissa		
Goat or Sheep Milk	Raw, Pasteurized, Boiled, flavoured and sterilized	Chandigarh		
		Haryana		
		Kerala		
		Madhya Pradesh and Chhatisgargh		
		Maharashtra		
		Punjab		
		Uttar Pradesh and Uttaranchal		
		Andaman & Nicobar		
		Andhra Pradesh		
		Assam		
		Bihar and Jharkhand	3.5	9.0
		Dadra & Nagar Haveli		
		Delhi		
		Goa, daman & diu		

(contd...)

Class of Milk	Designation	Locality	Minimum per cent	
			Milk fat	Milk solids non-fat
		Gujarat Himachal Pradesh Laccadive, Miniocoy & A. Islands Madras Manipur Mysore Nagaland NEFA Orissa Pondicherry Rajasthan Tripura West Bengal	3.0	9.3
Mixed Milk	Raw, Pasteurized, Boiled, Flavoured and Sterilized	All India	4.5	8.5
Standardized Milk	Pasteurized, Flavoured and Sterilized	All India	4.5	8.5
Recombine Milk	Pasteurized, Flavoured and Sterilized	All India	3.0	8.5
Toned Milk	Pasteurized, Flavoured and Sterilized	All India	3.0	8.5
Double Toned Milk	Pasteurized, Flavoured and Sterilized	All India	1.5	9.0
Skimmed Milk	Raw, Pasteurized, Boiled, Flavoured and Sterilized	All India	Not more than 0.5%	8.7

NOTE:

(1) When milk is offered for sale without any indication of the class, the standards prescribed from buffalo milk shall apply.

(2) The heat treatment for the various designated milk shall be as follows:

Designation	Heat Treatment
Raw	Nil
Pasteurized	Pasteurization
Boiled	Boiling
Flavoured	Pasteurization or Sterilization
Sterilized	Sterilization

MILK PRODUCTS

The products obtained from milk such as cream, *malai*, curd, skimmed milk curd, *chhenna*, skimmed milk *chhenna*, cheese, processed cheese, ice cream, milk ices, condensed milk sweetened and unsweetened, condensed skimmed milk sweetened and unsweetened, milk powder, skimmed milk powder, partly skimmed milk powder, *khoa*, infant milk food, table butter and *deshi* butter.

Milk Products shall not contain any substance not found in milk unless specified in the standards.

Cream excluding sterilized cream

Product of cow of buffalo milk or of a combination thereof which contains

Malai

The product rich in a buffer fat prepared by boiling and cooling cow or buffalo milk or a combination thereof. It shall contain not less than 25.0 per cent milk fat.

Dahi or Curd

The product obtained from pasteurized or boiled milk by souring, natural or otherwise, by a harmless lactic acid or other bacterial culture. *Dahi* may contain added cane sugar. *Dahi* shall have the same minimum percentage of milk fat and milk solids-not-fat as the milk from which it is prepared.

Where *dahi* or curd, other than skimmed milk *dahi*, is sold or offered for sale without any indication of class of milk, the standards prescribed for dahi prepared from buffalo milk shall apply.

Chhenna or *Paneer*

The product obtained from the cow or buffalo milk or a combination thereof by precipitation with sour milk, lactic acid or citric acid. It shall not contain more than 70.0 per cent moisture, and the milk fat content shall not be less than 50.0 per cent of the dry matter.

Skimmed Milk *Chhenna* or Skimmed Milk *Paneer*

The product obtained from cow or buffalo skimmed milk by precipitation with sour milk, lactic acid or citric acid. It shall not contain more than 70.0 per cent moisture. The milk fat content of the product shall not exceed 13.0 per cent of the dry matter.

Cheese (Hard)

The product obtained by draining after coagulation of milk with a harmless milk coagulating agent under the influence of harmless bacterial cultures. It shall not contain any ingredients not found in milk, except coagulating agents sodium chlorine, calcium chloride (anhydrous salt) not exceeding 0.02 per cent by weight, annatto or carotene colour, and may contain emulsifiers and/or stabilizers, namely citric acid, sodium citrate or sodium salts or orthophosphoric acid and polyphosphoric acid (as linear phosphate with a degree of polymerization up to 6 units), not exceeding 0.2 per cent by weight. Wax used for covering the outer surface shall not contain any thing harmful to health. In case the wax is coloured, only permitted food colour shall be used. Hard cheese shall contain not more than 43.0 per cent moisture and not less than 42.0 per cent milk fat of the dry matters. Hard cheese may contain 0.1 per cent of sorbic acid, or its sodium, potassium or calcium salt calculated as sorbic acid; or 0.1 per cent of nisin either singly or in combination.

Processed Cheese

The product obtained by heating cheese with permitted emulsifiers and/or stabilizers namely citric acid, sodium citrate, sodium salts of orthophosphoric acid and polyphosphoric acid (as linear polyphosphate with a degree of polymerization up to 6 units) with or without added condiments, and acidifying agents, namely vinegar, lactic acid, acetic acid, citric acid, and phosphoric acid. Processed cheese may contain not more than 4.0 per cent of anhydrous permitted emulsifiers and/or stabilizers provided that the content of anhydrous inorganic agents shall in no case exceed 3.0 per cent of the finished product. It shall not contain more than, 47.0 per cent moisture. The milk fat content shall not be less than 40.0 per cent of the dry matter. Processed cheese may contain 0.1 per cent sorbic acid or its sodium, potassium or calcium salts (calculated as sorbic acid) or 0.1 per cent of nisin.

Ice-Cream *Kulfi* and Chocolate Ice-Cream

Ice-cream *kulfi* and Chocolate ice-cream mean the frozen products obtained from cow or buffalo milk or a combination thereof or from cream, and/or other milk product, with or without the addition of cane sugar, eggs, fruit juices, preserved fruits, nuts, chocolate, edible flavours and permitted food colours. It may contain permitted stabilizers and emulsifiers not exceeding 0.5 per cent by weight. The mixture shall be suitably heated before freezing. The product shall contain not less than 10.0 per cent milk fat, 3.5 per cent protein and 36.0 per cent total solid except that when any of the aforesaid preparations contains fruits or nuts or both, the content of milk fat may proportionately be reduced but shall not be less than 8.0 per cent by weight.

Starch may be added to a maximum extent of 5.0 per cent of under a declaration on a label as specified in sub-rule (2) of Rule 43.

The standards for ice-cream shall also apply to softy ice-cream.

Milk Ices or Milk Lollies

These frozen products obtained from milk, skimmed milk, or milk product with or without the addition of cane sugar, eggs, fruits, juices, nuts, chocolate, edible flavours, and permitted food colours. It may contain permitted stabilizers not exceeding 0.5 per cent of the product. The mixture shall be suitably heat-treated before freezing. The product shall contain not more than 2.0 per cent milk fat, no less than 3.5 per cent proteins and not less than 20.0 per cent total solids.

Condensed Milk Unsweetened (Evaporated Milk)

The product obtained from cow or buffalo milk or a combination thereof or from standardized milk, by the partial removal of water. It may contain added calcium chloride, citric acid and sodium citrate, sodium salt or orthophosphoric acid and polyphosphoric acid (as linear phosphate with a degree of polymerization up to 6 units) not exceeding 0.3 per cent by weight of the finished product. Such additions need not be declared on the table. Condensed milk unsweetened shall contain not less than 8.0 per cent milk fat and not less than 26.0 per cent milk solids.

Condensed Milk Sweetened

The product obtained from cow or buffalo milk or a combination thereof or from standardized milk by the partial removal of water and after addition of cane sugar. It may contain added refined lactose, (permitted flavour), calcium chloride, citric acid, sodium citrate, sodium salts of orthophosphoric and polyphosphoric acid (as linear phosphate with a degree of polymerization up to 6 units) not exceeding 0.3 per cent by weight of the finished product. Such addition need not be declared on the label. Condensed milk sweetened shall contain not less than 9.0 per cent milk fat, not less than 31.0 per cent total milk solids and not less than 40.0 per cent cane sugar.

Condensed Skimmed Milk Unsweetened (Evaporated Skimmed Milk)

The product obtained from cow or buffalo skimmed milk or a combination thereof by the partial removal of water. It may contain added calcium chloride, citric acid, and sodium citrate, sodium salt of orthophosphoric acid and polyphosphoric acid (as linear phosphate with a degree of polymerization up to 6 units) not exceeding 0.3 per cent by weight of the finished product. Such addition need not be declared on the label. Condensed skimmed milk unsweetened shall contain not less than 20.0 per cent total milk solids. The fat content shall not exceed 0.5 per cent by weight.

Condensed Skimmed Milk Sweetened

The product obtained from cow or buffalo skimmed milk or a combination thereof by the partial removal of water and after addition of cane sugar. It may contain added refined lactose, calcium chloride citric acid and sodium citrate, sodium salts of orthophosphoric acid, and polyphosphoric acid (as linear phosphate with a degree of polymerization up to 6 units) not exceeding 0.3 per cent by weight of the finished product. Such addition need not be declared on the label. Condensed skimmed milk sweetened shall contain not less than 26.0 per cent of total milk solids and not less than 40.0 per cent cane sugar. The fat content shall not exceed 0.5 per cent by weight.

Milk Powder

The product obtained from cow or buffalo milk or a combination thereof or from standardized milk, by the removal of water. It may contain calcium chloride, citric acid and sodium citrate, sodium salts of orthophosphoric acid and polyphosphoric acid (as linear phosphate with a degree of polymerization up to 6 units) not exceeding 0.3 per cent by weight of the finished product and 0.01 per cent of butylated hydroxyanisole (BHA) by weight of the finished product. Such addition need not be declared on the label. For improving dispensability, it may contain lecithin to a maximum limit of 0.5 per cent under label declaration as per Rule 42(ee). Milk powder shall contain not more than 5.0 per cent moisture and not less than 26.0 per cent milk fat. The maximum acidity expressed as lactic acid shall not be more than 1.2 per cent. The plate count shall not exceed 50,000 per gram and *E. coli* shall not exceed 90 per gram or solubility index of the product shall be as follows:

		Roller-dried	Spray-dried
Solubility per cent (minimum)	:	85.0	98.5

Coliform count of the powder shall not be more than 90 per gram.

The process of drying shall be mentioned on the label. The spray-dried product shall be packed in hermetically sealed containers when the net quantity exceeds 510 grams.

Skimmed Milk Powder

The product obtained from cow or buffalo milk or a combination thereof by the removal of water. It may contain added calcium chloride, citric acid sodium citrate, sodium salts of orthophosphoric acid and polymerization up to 6 units) not exceeding 0.3 per cent by weight of the finished product. Such addition need not be declared on the label. Skimmed milk product shall not contain more than 1.5 per cent milk fat and moisture shall not exceed 50 per cent. The total acidity expressed as lactic acid shall not exceed 1.5 per cent. The plate count shall exceed 50,000 par gram and *E. coli* shall not exceed 90 per gram. The solubility index of the product shall be as follows:

		Roller-dried	Spray-dried
Solubility per cent (minimum)	:	85.0	98.5

The process of drying shall be mentioned on the label.

Partly Skimmed Milk Powder

The product obtained from partly skimmed cow or buffalo milk or a combination thereof by the removal of water. It may contain added calcium chloride, citric acid and sodium citrate, sodium salts of orthophosphoric acid and polyphosphoric acid (as linear phosphate with a degree of polymerization up to 6 units) not be exceeding 0.3 per cent by weight of the finished product. Such addition need not be declared on the label. Partly skimmed milk powder shall not contain more than 5.0 per cent moisture and fat content of the product shall be between 1.6 and 24.0 per cent. Butylated hydroxyanisole (BHA) not exceeding 0.01 per cent by weight of the finished product may be added. The exact fat content shall be indicated on the label. The minimum solubility/solubility index of the product shall conform to the following standards:

	Roller-dried	Spray-dried
Solubility per cent (minimum) :	85.0	98.5

The process of drying shall be mentioned on the label. The spray-dried product shall be packed in hermetically sealed containers when the net quantity exceed 510 grams.

Partly Skimmed Milk Powder (sour)

Partly skimmed milk powder (sour) used by industry like bakery may contain sodium bicarbonate as a neutralizer, provided that the resultant product is labelled as 'UNFIT FOR DIRECT CONSUMPTION". The amount of food additives including neutralizers added shall, however, be same as prescribed for partly skimmed milk powder. It shall also conform to other standards prescribed for partly skimmed milk powder except that solubility percentage will be 75 per cent, minimum by weight.

Khoya

The product obtained from cow/buffalo/goat/sheep milk or a combination thereof by rapid drying. The milk fat content shall not be less than 20 per cent of the finished product.

Infant Milk Food

The infant milk food obtained by drying cow or buffalo milk or a combination thereof or by drying standardized milk; with the addition of specific carbohydrates (cane sugar, dextrose, and dextrins, maltose or lactose), iron salts and vitamins. It shall be free from starch and antioxidants. Its moisture content shall not be more than 5.0 per cent. Milk fat content not less than 18.0 per cent and not more than 28.0 per cent, total carbohydrates not less than 35.0 per cent milk protein not less than 20.0 per cent, total ash not more than 8.5 per cent, ash insoluble in dilute hydrochloric acid, not more than 0.05 per cent, iron (as Fe) not less than 4.0 mg/100g; and vitamin A content not less than 15 I U/g. The process used in drying shall be indicated on the label. Infant milk food shall not be show Standard Plate Count of more than 50,000 per gram. The solubility index of the product shall conform to the following standards:

		Roller-Dried	Spray-dried
Solubility per cent (minimum)	:	85.0 ml.	98.5 ml.

The product shall be packed in hermetically sealed containers and the label shall bear the date by which the product is to be consumed.

TABLE (CREAMERY) BUTTER

The table butter obtained from cow or buffalo milk or a combination thereof or from cream or curd obtained from cow or buffalo milk or a combination thereof with or without the addition of common salt and annatto or carotene as colouring matter. It shall be free from other animal fats, wax and mineral oils, vegetable oils and fats. No preservative except common salt and no colouring matter except annatto or carotene shall be added. It shall contain not less than 80.0 per cent by weight of milk fats, not more than 1.5 per cent by weight of curd and not more than 3.0 per cent by weight of common salt. Diacetyl may be added as a flavouring agent but, if so used, the total diacetyl content shall not exceed 4.0 parts per million. Calcium hydroxide, sodium bicarbonate, sodium carbonate, sodium polyphosphate, (as linear phosphate with a degree of polymerization hp to 7 units) may be added for regulating the hydrogen ion concentration in the finished product not exceeding 0.2 per cent by weight of butter as a whole.

DESHI (COOKING) BUTTER

The deshi butter obtained from cow or buffalo milk or a combination thereof of curd obtained from cow or buffalo milk or a combination thereof without the addition of any preservative including common salt, any added colouring matter or any added flavouring agent. It shall be free from other animal fats, wax and mineral oils, vegetable oils and fats. It shall contain not less then 76.0 per cent of milk fat by weight:

Provided that where butter is sold or offered for sale without any indication as to whether it is table butter or deshi butter, the standards of quality prescribed for table butter shall apply.

GHEE (PURE CLARIFIED FAT)

The pure clarified fat derived solely from mil or from curd or from *deshi* (cooking) butter or from cream to which no colouring matter or preservative has been added. The standard of quality of *ghee* produced in a State or Union Territory specified in column 2 of the Table 3.2 shall be as specified against the said State or Union Territory in the corresponding column 3, 4, 5 and 6 of the said Table 3.2.

Table 3.2: Standard of Quality of *Ghee* in Different States

Sl. No.	Name of state/ Union territory	Butyro-refractometer reading at 400°C	Minimum Reichert value	Percentage	
				Free fatty acid as oleic acid (maximum	Mois-ture (max. limit) limit)
1.	Andhra Pradesh	40.0 to 43.0	24	3.0	0.5
2.	Assam	40.0 to 43.0	26	3.0	0.5
3.	Bihar and Jharkhand	40.0 to 43.0	28	3.0	0.5
4.	Delhi	40.0 to 43.0	28	3.0	0.5
5.	Gujarat –				
	(a) Area other than cotton tract areas	40.0 to 43.5	24	3.0	0.5
	(b) Cotton tract areas	41.5 to 45.0	21	3.0	
6.	Himachal Pradesh	40.0 to 43.0	26	3.0	0.5
7.	Kerala	40.0 to 43.0	26	3.0	0.5
8.	Madhya Pradesh Chhandigarh				

(Contd. . .)

1	2	3	4	5	6
	(a) Areas other than the erstwhile State of Bhopal, Vindhya Pradesh and Cotton Tract areas	40.0 to 43.0	26	3.0	0.5
	(b) Territories of the erstwhile States of Bhopal and Vindhya Pradesh	40.0 to 43.0	28	3.0	0.5
	(c) Cotton tract areas	41.5 to 45.0	21	3.0	0.5
9.	Tamil Nadu	41.0 to 44.0	24	3.0	0.5
10.	Manipur	40.0 to 43.0	26	3.0	0.5
11.	Mysore –				
	(a) Areas other than Belgaum district	40.0 to 44.0	24	3.0	0.5
	(b) Belgaum district	40.0 to 44.0	26	3.0	0.5
12.	Maharashtra –				
	(a) Cotton tract area	41.5 to 45.0	21	3.0	0.5
	(b) Other areas	40.0 to 43.0	26	3.0	0.5
13.	Orissa	40.0 to 43.0	26	3.0	0.5
14.	Punjab and Haryana				
	(a) Areas other than Mahendragarh	40.0 to 43.0	28	3.0	0.5
	(b) Mahendragarh	40.0 to 43.0	26	3.0	0.5
15.	Rajasthan –				
	(a) Areas other than Jodhpur Division	40.0 to 43.0	26	3.0	0.5
	(b) Jodhpur Division	41.5 to 45.0	21	3.0	0.5
16.	Tripura	40.0 to 43.0	28	3.0	0.5
17.	U.P. and Uttaranchal	40.0 to 43.0	28	3.0	0.5
18.	West Bengal –				
	(a) Areas other than Bishnupur Sub-Division	40.0 to 43.0	28	3.0	0.5
	(b) Bishnupur Sub-Division	41.5 to 45.0	21	3.0	0.5

Note: Baudouin test shall be negative.

But cotton tract is meant the areas in the States where cotton seed is extensively fed to the little and so notified by the State Government concerned.

CHAPTER 4

TEA AND COFFEE

Tea, other than Kangra tea derived exclusively from the leaves, buds and tender stems of plants of *Camellia* genus and the species, and includes (i) leaf, (ii) broken, (iii) fanning and (iv) dust. It shall conform to the following specifications:

Total ash determined on tea dried to constant weight at 100°C	:	5.0 to 9.0%
Total ash soluble in boiling distilled water	:	Note less than 40.0% of total ash
Ash insoluble in HCl	:	Not more than 1.0%
Extract obtained by boiling dry tea (dried to constant weight at 100°C) with 100 parts of distilled water for one hour under reflux	:	Not less than 32%
Alkalinity of soluble ash	:	Not less than 1.0 per cent and not more than 2.2 per cent expressed as K_2O.
Crude fibre determined on tea dried	:	Not more than 17% to a constant weight at 1000°C.

It shall not contain any added colouring matter.

KANGRA TEA

Tea derived exclusively from the leaves, buds and tender stems of plants of the *Camellia sinensis* or *Camellia* tea grown in Kangra and Mandi Vallleys of Himachal Pradesh. It shall conform to the following specifications, namely:

Total ash determined on tea dried to constant weight at 100°C	:	4.5 to 9.0%
Total ash soluble in boiling distilled water	:	Not less than 34.0% of total ash
Ash insoluble in HCl	:	Not more than 1.2%
Extract obtained by boiling dry tea (dried to constant weight at 100°C) with 100 parts of distilled water for one hour under reflux	:	Not less than 23%
Alkalinity of soluble ash	:	Not less than 1.0% and not more than 2.2% expressed as K_2O.
Crude fibre determined on tea dried	:	Not more than 17% to a constant weight at 1000°C.

It shall not contain any added colouring matter:

COFFEE

Coffee (green, raw or unroasted) means the seed of *Coffea arabica*, *Coffee arabica*, *Coffee liberica*; *Coffee excelsa* or, *Coffea robusted* freed from all but a small portion of its supermodern by decortication.

Roasted coffee means properly cleaned green coffee which has been roasted to a brown colour and has developed its characteristic aroma.

Ground coffee means the powdered product obtained from 'roasted coffee' only and shall be free from husk.

Coffee (green, raw or unroasted) 'roasted coffee' and 'ground coffee' shall be free from any artificial colouring, flavouring, facing, extraneous matter or glazing substance and shall be in sound, dry and fresh condition free from rancid or obnoxious flavour.

'**Roasted coffee**' and '**ground coffee**' shall conform to the following analytical standards:

(i) Total ash (determined on the sample dried to constant weight at 100°C) shall be feathery white or bluish-white in colour and shall be not less than 3.0 per cent and not more than 6.0 per cent by weight of which not less than 65 per cent shall be soluble in boiling distilled water. The ash insoluble in hot dilute HCl shall not be more than 0.1 per cent.

(ii) The alkalinity of the soluble ash per gram of dried coffee shall be equivalent to not less than 3.5 ml. and not more than 4.5 ml. of N/10 acid.

(iii) The caffeine content as obtained by standards methods, shall be not less than 1.0 per cent.

(iv) The acqeous extract (determined by extraction of 2-grams of the sample dried to constant weight at 100°C with 100 ml. of boiling distilled water for one hour under reflux) shall be not less than 26.0 per cent and not more than 35.0 per cent.

CHICORY

Means the roasted chicory powder obtained by roasting the cleaned and dried roots of *Chicorium intybus* Lin. with or without the addition of edible fats and oils or sugar like glucose or sucrose in proportion not exceeding 2.0 per cent by weight in aggregate. It shall be free any artificial colouring and flavouring matter.

It shall conform to the following standards:

Total ash	:	Not more than 3.5 per cent and not less than 10.0 per cent (on dry basis)
Ash insoluble in dilute HCl	:	Not more than 2.5 per cent by dry basis.
Water Soluble	:	Not less than 50.0 per cent on dry matter basis.

COFFEE CHICORY

Mixture or coffee mixed with chicory or coffee and chicory shall be pure ground coffee mixed with roasted and ground chicory and shall be in sound, dry and dust-free condition with no rancid or obnoxious flavour.

The coffee chicory mixture shall contain caffeine not less than 0.6 per cent and the aqueous extract shall not be more than 50 per cent.

Any tin or other receptacle containing a mixture of coffee and chicory shall not bear any misleading expression.

The expression "French Coffee" may be used if followed by the words "mixed with chicory" or "blended with chicory".

CHAPTER 5

SPICES, CONDIMENTS AND PAN MASALA

CARAWAY (*SIAHJIRA*)

Whole caraway means the dried seed of the plant *Carum carvi* (L). Extraneous matter including foreign edible seeds, chaff, stem, straw, dust, dirt, stones and lumps of earth shall not exceed 5 per cent by weight.

The amount of insect damaged matter shall not exceed 5 per cent by weight.

The term 'insect damaged matter' means spices that are partially or wholly bored by insect.

CARAWAY (*SIAHJIRA*) POWDER

Means the powder obtained from the dried seeds of *Carum carvi* (L). It may be in the form of small pieces of the seeds or in finely ground form. It shall conform to the following standards:

Moisture	:	Not more than 13.0 per cent by weight.
Total ash	:	Not more than 8.0 per cent by weight.
Ash insoluble in dilute HCl	:	Not more than 1.5 per cent by weight.

CARAWAY BLACK (*CARUM BULBOCASTENUM*) (*SIAHJEERA*)

Means the dried seeds of *Carum bulbocastanum*. It shall conform to the following standards:

Foreign edible seeds	:	Not more than 5.0 per cent by weight.
Total ash	:	Not more than 9.0 per cent by weight.
Ash insoluble of dilute HCl	:	Not more than 1.5 per cent by weight.

The amount of insect damaged matter shall not exceed 5 per cent by weight.

The term 'insect damaged matter' means spices that are partially or wholly bored by insects.

CARDAMON (*CHHOTI ELACHI*)

Whole means the dried, nearly ripe fruits of *Elettaria cardamomum* (L). The percentage of extraneous matter shall not exceed 5.0 per cent by weight. The cardamom seeds obtained from the capsules shall contain not less than 3.0 per cent (v/w) of volatile oil.

The amount of insect damaged matter shall not exceed 5 per cent by weight.

The term 'insect damaged matter' means spices that are partially or wholly bored by insects.

CARDAMOM (*CHHOTI ELACHI*) SEEDS

Means the seeds obtained by separating the seeds from the capsules of *Elettaria cardamomum* (L). The percentage of extraneous matter in the seeds shall not exceed 2.0 per cent by weight. The seeds shall contain not less than 3.0 per cent (v/w) of volatile oil.

The amount of insect damaged matter shall not exceed 5 per cent by weight.

The term 'insect damaged matter' means spices that are partially or wholly bored by insects.

CARDAMOM (*CHHOTI ELACHI*) POWDER

Means the powder obtained from the seeds separated from the capsules of *Elettaria cardamomum* (L). It may be in the form of small pieces of the seeds or in finely ground form. It shall conform to the following standards:

Moisture	:	Not more than 14.0 per cent by weight.
Total ash	:	Not more than 8.0 per cent by weight.
Volatile oil	:	Not less than 3.0 per cent (v/w)
Ash insoluble in dilute HCl	:	Not more than 3.0 per cent by weight.

CARDAMOM AMOMUM (*BADI ELACHI*)

Whole Cardamom means the dried, nearly ripe fruit of *Amomum subulatum* Roxb. In the form of capsules. The proportion of calyx pieces, stalk bits and other extraneous matter shall not exceed 5.0 per cent by weight. The *Cardamom amomum* seeds obtained from the capsules shall contain not less than 1.0 per cent (v/w) of volatile oil.

The amount of insect damaged matter shall not exceed 5 per cent by weight.

The term 'insect damaged matter' means spices that are partially or wholly bored by insects.

CARDAMOM AMOMUM (*BADI ELACHI*) SEEDS

Means the seeds obtained by separating the seeds from the cardamom amomum capsules of *Amomum subulatum* Roxb. The percentage of extraneous matter in seeds shall not exceed 2.0 per cent by weight. The seeds shall contain not less than 1.0 per cent (v/w) volatile oil.

The amount of insect damaged matter shall not exceed 5 per cent by weight.

The term 'insect damaged matter' means spices that are partially or wholly bored by insects.

CARDAMOM AMOMUM (*BADI ELACHI*) POWDER

Means the powder obtained from the seeds separated from the capsules of *Amomum subulatum* Roxb. It may be in the form of small pieces of the seeds or in finely ground form. It shall conform to the following standards:

Moisture	:	Not more than 14.0 per cent by weight.
Total ash	:	Not more than 8.0 per cent by weight.
Volatile oil	:	Not less than 1.0 per cent (v/w)
Ash insoluble in dilute HCl	:	Not more than 3.0 per cent by weight.

CHILLIES (*LAL MIRCHI*)

Whole chillies mean the dried ripe fruits or pods of *Capsicum annum*/ *Capsicum frutescens* (L). The proportion of extraneous matter including calyx pieces, loose tops, dirt, lumps of earth, stones shall not exceed 5.0 per cent by weight. The pods shall be free from extraneous colouring matter, coating of mineral oil and other harmful substances.

The amount of insect damaged matter shall not exceed 5 per cent by weight.

The term 'insect damaged matter' means spices that are partially or wholly bored by insects.

CHILLIES (*LAL MIRCHI*) POWDER

Means the powder obtained by grinding dried chilli pods of *Capsicum frutescens* L./*Capsicum annum*. The chilli powder shall be dry, free from dirt, mould growth, insect infestation, extraneous matter, added colouring matter and flavouring matter. The chilli powder may contain any edible oil to a maximum limit of 2 per cent by weight under a label declaration for the amount and the nature of oil used. The chilli powder shall conform to the following standards:

Moisture	:	Not more than 12.0 per cent by weight.
Total ash	:	Not more than 8.0 per cent by weight.
Ash soluble in dilute HCl	:	Not more than 1.3 per cent by weight.
Non-volatile ether extract	:	Not more than 1.3 per cent by weight.
Non-volatile ether extract	:	Not less than 12.0 per cent by weight.
Crude fibre	:	Not more than 300 per cent by weight.

CINNAMON (*DALCHINI*)

Whole Cinnamon means the dried pieces of the inner bark of *Cinnamomum zeylanicum* blume. It shall not contain any other foreign vegetable matter or colouring matter. It shall contain not less than 0.5 per cent (v/w) of volatile oil.

The amount of insect damaged matter shall not exceed 5 per cent by weight.

The term 'insect damaged matter' means spices that are partially or wholly bored by insects.

CINNAMON (*DALCHINI*) POWDER

Means the powder obtained by grinding the dried inner bark of *Cinnamomum zeylanicum* (Blume). The cinnamon powder shall conform to the following standards:

Moisture	:	Not more than 12.0 per cent by weight.
Total ash	:	Not more than 8.0 per cent by weight.
Ash soluble in dilute HCl	:	Not more than 2.0 per cent by weight.
Volatile oil	:	Not more than 0.5 per cent (v/w).

CASSIA TAJ (WHOLE)

Means dried pieces of bark of *Cinnamomum cassia* Blume, Syn, *Cinnamomum arometicum*. Nees (*Chinse Cinnamon*, or *Cassia lignea*). It shall not contain any other foreign vegetable matter or colouring matter.

CLOVES (*LAUNG*)

Whole cloves means the dried unopened flower buds of *Eugenia caryophyllate* Thumb. The extraneous matter shall not exceed 5.0 per cent by weight. The cloves shall contain not less than 15.0 per cent (v/w) of volatile oil.

The amounts of insect damaged matter shall not exceed 5 per cent by weight.

The term 'insect damaged matter' means spices that are partially or wholly bored by insects.

CLOVES (*LAUNG*) POWDER

Means the powder obtained by grinding the dried unopened flower buds of *Eugenia caryophyllate* thumb. The cloves powder shall conform to the following standards:

Moisture	:	Not more than 12.0 per cent by weight.
Total ash	:	Not more than 7.0 per cent by weight.
Ash soluble in dilute HCl	:	Not more than 0.5 per cent by weight.
Volatile oil	:	Not more than 15.0 per cent (v/w).

CORIANDER (*DHANIA*)

Whole Coriander means the dried nature fruits (seeds) of *Coriandrum sativum* (L). The proportion of extraneous matter including dust, dirt, stones, lumps of earth, chaff, stalk, stem or straw, edible seeds of fruits other than coriander and insect damaged seeds shall not exceed 8.0 per cent by weight.

The amount of insect damaged matter shall not exceed 5 per cent by weight.

The term 'insect damaged matter' means spices that are partially or wholly bored by insects.

CORIANDER (*DHANIA*) POWDER

Coriander powder means the powder obtained by grinding clean dried coriander fruits of *Coriandrum sativum* (L). It shall be in the form of a rough or fine powder. It shall conform to the following standards.

Moisture	:	Not more than 12.0 per cent by weight.
Total ash	:	Not more than 7.0 per cent by weight.
Ash soluble in dilute HCl	:	Not more than 1.5 per cent by weight.

CUMIN (*SAFED JEERA*)

Whole cumin means the dried seeds of *Cuminum cyminum* (L). The proportion of extraneous matter including dust, stones, lumps of earth, chaff, stem or straw shall not exceed 7.0 per cent by weight. The proportion of edible seed other than cumin seeds shall not exceed 5.0 per cent by weight.

The amount of insect damaged matter shall not exceed 5 per cent by weight.

The term 'insect damaged matter' means spices that are partially or wholly bored by insects.

CUMIN (*SAFED JEERA*) POWDER

Cumin Powder means the powder obtained by grinding the dried seeds of *Cuminum cyminum* L. The powder shall conform to the following standards:

Moisture	:	Not more than 12.0 per cent by weight.
Total ash	:	Not more than 8.5 per cent by weight.

Ash soluble in dilute HCl	:	Not more than 1.5 per cent by weight.

CUMIN BLACK (*KALONJI*)

Whole cumin means the dried seeds of *Nigella sativa* L. The proportion of extraneous matter including dust, dirt, stones, lumps of earth, chaff, stem or straw shall not exceed 7.0 per cent by weight. The proportion of edible seeds other than cumin black shall not exceed 5.0 per cent by weight.

The amount of insect damaged matter shall not exceed 5 per cent by weight.

Explanation: The term 'insect damaged matter' means spices that are partially or wholly bored by insects.

CUMIN BLACK (*KALONJI*) POWDER

Cumin black powder means the powder obtained by grinding the dried seeds of *Nigella sativa* L. The powder shall conform to the following standards:

Moisture	:	Not more than 12.0 per cent by weight.
Total ash	:	Not more than 7.0 per cent by weight.
Ash soluble in dilute HCl	:	Not more than 1.5 per cent by weight.
Volatile oil	:	Not less than 0.5 per cent (v/w)

FENNEL (*SAUNF*)

Whole fennel (*saunf*) means the dried ripe fruits of *Foeniculum vulgare* Mill. The proportion of extraneous matter including dust, dirt, stone, lumps of earth, chaff, stem or straw shall not exceed 5.0 per cent by weight. The proportion of edible seeds other than fennel shall not exceed 5.0 per cent by weight.

The amount of insect damaged matter shall not exceed 5 per cent by weight.

The term 'insect damaged matter' means spices that are partially or wholly bored by insects.

FENNEL (*SAUNF*) POWDER

Fennel (*saunf*) powder means the powder obtained by grinding the dried ripe fruits of *Foeniculum vulgare* Mill. The powder shall conform to the following standards:

Moisture	:	Not more than 12.0 per cent by weight.
Total ash	:	Not more than 9.0 per cent by weight.
Ash soluble in dilute HCl	:	Not more than 2.0 per cent by weight.
Volatile oil	:	Not less than 1.0 per cent (v/w)

FENUGREEK (*METHI*)

Whole fenugreek means the dried ripe seeds of *Trigonella foanum-groecum* L. The proportion of extraneous matter including dust, dirt, stones, lumps of earth, chaff, stem or straw shall not exceed 5.0 per cent by weight. The proportion of edible seeds other than fenugreek shall not exceed 5.0 per cent by weight.

The amount of insect damaged matter shall not exceed 5 per cent by weight.

The term 'insect damaged matter' means spices that are partially or wholly bored by insects.

FENUGREEK (*METHI*) POWDER

Fenugreek (*Methi*) powder means the powder obtained by grinding the dried ripe seeds of *Trigonella foenumgroecum* L. The powder shall conform to the following standards:

Moisture	:	Not more than 10.0 per cent by weight.
Total ash	:	Not more than 7.0 per cent by weight.
Ash soluble in dilute HCl	:	Not more than 2.0 per cent by weight.

Cold water in dilute HCl	:	Not less than 30.0 per cent by weight.

GINGER (*SONTH, ADRAK*)

Whole ginger means the rhizomes of *Zingiber officinale* rose in pieces irregular in shape and size with peel not entirely removed, washed and dried in the sun. The proportion of extraneous matter shall not exceed 2.0 per cent by weight. It shall contain on dry basis not less than 1.0 per cent (v/w) of volatile oil. If the ginger is limed, the lime (Calcium oxide) content shall not exceed 4.0 per cent by weight on dry basis.

The amount of insect damaged matter shall not exceed 5 per cent by weight.

The term 'insect damaged matter' means spices that are partially or wholly bored by insects.

GINGER (*SONTH, ADRAK*) POWDER

Ginger powder means the powder obtained by grinding ginger (*Zingiber officinale* rose) whole. The powder shall conform to the following standards:

Moisture	:	Not more than 13.0 per cent by weight.
Total ash	:	Not more than 8.0 per cent by weight.
Ash soluble in dilute HCl	:	Not more than 1.0 per cent by weight.
Water soluble ash	:	Not less than 1.7 per cent by weight.
Cold water soluble extract	:	Not less than 1.7 per cent by weight.
Calcium (as CaO)	:	Not more than 4.0 per cent by weight on dry basis.
Alcohol (90% v/w) soluble extract	:	Not less than 4.5 per cent by weight.

Volatile oil : Not less than 1.0 per cent v/w).

MACE (*JAEPATRI*)

Whole means the dried coat or arilus of the seed of *Myristica fragrans* Houtt. It shall not contain the arilus of any other variety of *Myristica nalabarica* or Fatua (*Bombay mace*) and *Myristica argentea* (Wild mace). The proportion of extraneous matter shall not exceed 3.0 per cent by weight.

MACE (*JAEPATRI*) POWDER

Mace powder means the powder obtained by grinding the dried coat or arilus of the seed *Myristica fragrans* Houtt. The powder shall conform the following standards:

Moisture	:	Not more than 10.0 per cent by weight.
Total ash	:	Not more than 3.0 per cent by weight.
Ash soluble in dilute HCl	:	Not more than 1.0 per cent by weight.
Crude fibre	:	Not more than 10.0 per cent by weight.
Non-volatile ether extract	:	Not less than 20.0 and not more than 30.0 per cent by weight.

The amount of insect damaged matter shall not exceed 5 per cent by weight.

The term 'insect damaged matter' means spices that are partially or wholly bored by insects.

MUSTARD (*RAI, SARSON*)

Whole mustard means the dried seeds of *Brassica alba* (L.) Boiss (*safed rai*), *Brassica compestris* L. var *dichotoma* (*kali sarson*) *Brassica compestris* L. var. yellow *sarson*, Syn. *Brassica compestris* L. var. glauca (*pili sarson*), *Brassica compestris* L. var. *toria* (*Toria*), *Brassica juncea* (L), *Cosset czern* (*Rai, Lotni*) and *Brassica nigra* (L.) *Koch* (*Benarsi Rai*). The proportion of extraneous matter which includes dust, dirt, stones, lumps of earth chaff, stem, straw, edible food-grains, edible oilseeds of any other variety or any other impurity shall not exceed 7.0 per cent by weight. It shall be free seeds of *Argemone mexicana* Linn.

The amount of insect damaged matter shall not exceed 5 per cent by weight.

The term 'insect damaged matter' means spices that are partially or wholly bored by insects.

MUSTARD (*RAI, SARSON*) POWDER

Means the powder obtained by grinding the dried seeds of *Brassica alba* (L.) *Boiss* (*safed rai*), *Brassica compestris* L. var. dichotoma (*kali sarson*), *Brassica compestris* L. var. (*yellow Sarson*), Syn. *Brassica compestris* L. var. glauca (*Pili Sarson*), *Brassica compestris* L. var. *toria* (*toria*), *Brassica juncea*, (L.) Coss. Et. Czern, (*Rai, Lotni*) and *Brassica nigra* (L.) Koch. (*benarsi rai*). The powder shall conform to the following standards:

Moisture	:	Not more than 7.0 per cent by weight.
Total ash	:	Not more than 8.0 per cent by weight.
Volatile oil	:	Not less than 0.25 per cent v/w.
Non-volatile ether extract	:	Not less than 22.0 per cent by weight.
Ash insoluble in dilute HCl	:	Not more than 2.0 per cent by weight
Crude fibre	:	Not more than 8.0 per cent by weight.
Starch	:	Not more than 15.0 per cent by weight.

The test for argemone oil shall be negative.

NUTMEG (*JAIPHAL*)

Whole nutmeg means the dried seeds of *Myristica fragrans* Houtt. The proportion of extraneous matter and infestation shall not exceed 3.0 per cent by weight.

NUTMEG (*JAIPHAL*) POWDER

Nutmeg (*jaiphal*) powder means the powder obtained by grinding the dried seeds of Myristica fragrans Houtt. The powder shall conform to the following standards:

Moisture	:	Not more than 8.0 per cent by weight.
Total ash	:	Not more than 5.0 per cent by weight.
Ash insoluble in dilute HCl	:	Not more than 0.5 per cent by weight
Non-volatile ether extract	:	Not less than 25.0 per cent by weight.
Crude fibre	:	Not more than 10.0 per cent by weight.

PEPPER BLACK (*KALI MIRCH*)

Whole pepper black means the dried berries of *Piper nigrum* L. brown to black in colour with wrinkled surface. The proportion of extraneous matter including dust, stalks, leafy matter and other foreign matter shall not exceed 3.0 per cent by weight. The proportion by weight of light berries and pinheads shall not exceed 10.0 per cent and 4.0 per cent respectively.

The amount of insect damaged matter shall not exceed 5 per cent by weight.

The term 'insect damaged matter' means spices that are partially or wholly bored by insects.

PEPPER BLACK (*KALI MIRCH*) POWDER

Pepper black powder means the powder obtained by grinding the dried berries of *Piper nigrum* L. and shall be without the addition of any other matter. The powder shall conform to the following standards:

Moisture	:	Not more than 12.5 per cent by weight.
Total ash	:	Not more than 8.0 per cent by weight.
Ash insoluble in dilute HCl	:	Not more than 1.2 per cent by weight
Non-volatile ether extract	:	Not less than 5.5 per cent by weight.
Crude fibre	:	Not more than 18.0 per cent by weight.

LIGHT BLACK PEPPER

Means the dried berries of *Piper nigrum* L. dark brown to dark black in colour. It shall be well dried and free from mould or insects and shall not contain more than 6 per cent extraneous matters including dust, stone, lump of earth, stalks, leafy matters and other foreign edible seeds and 10 per cent pinheads.

PINHEADS

Shall be wholly derived from the spikes of *Piper nigrum*. They shall be reasonably dry and free from insects. The colour shall be from dark brown to black. The extraneous matter shall not exceed 7 per cent.

POPPY (*KHAS-KHAS*)

Whole poppy means the dried seeds of the ripe fruit of *Papaver somniferum* L. The seed may be white or grayish in colour. The proportion of extraneous matter shall not exceed 15.0 per cent by weight. It shall contain not less than 40.0 per cent by weight of non-volatile ether extract.

SAFFRON (*KESAR*)

Saffron means the dried stigmata or tops of styles of *Crocus sativus* L. It shall not contain any foreign colouring matter or any other extraneous matter. It shall conform to the following standards:

Total ash	:	Not more than 8% by weight.

Ash insoluble	:	Not more than 1.5% by weight in dilute HCl
Volatile-matter at 103° ± 1°C.	:	Not more than 14% by weight
Aqueous extract	:	Not less than 55% by weight
Total Nitrogen (on dry weight basis)	:	Not less than 5% by weight
Foreign matter such as dirt, earth, dust, leaf, seem, chaff and vegetable matter.	:	Not more than 1%.
Floral waste defined as yellow filaments, pollen, segments, parts of ovary and other arts of flowers of *Crocus sativus* Linn.	:	Not more than 15.

Saffron shall be free from living insects, moulds and shall be practically free from dead insect, insect-fragments and rodent contamination visible to naked eye.

TURMERIC (*HALDI*)

Whole tumeric means the dried rhizome or bulbous roots of the plant of *Curcuma longa* L. It shall be free from lead chromate and other artificial colouring matter. The proportion of extraneous matter shall not exceed 2.0 per cent by weight.

The amount of insect damaged matter shall not exceed 5 per cent by weight.

The term 'insect damaged matter' means spices that are partially or wholly bored by insects.

TURMERIC (*HALDI*) POWDER

Turmeric powder means the powder obtained by grinding the dried rhizomes or bulbous roots of the plant of *Curcuma longa*

L. It shall be free from artificial colouring matter. The powder shall conform to the following standards:

Moisture	:	Not more than 13.0 per cent by weight.
Total ash	:	Not more than 9.0 per cent by weight.
Ash insoluble in dilute HCl	:	Not more than 1.5 per cent by weight
Test for lead chromate	:	Negative
Total starch percent by weight	:	Not more than 60.0 per cent

CURRY POWDER

Means the powder obtained from grinding clean, dried and sound spices belonging to the group of aromatic herbs and seeds such as black pepper, cinnamon, cloves, coriander, cardamon, chillies, cumin seeds, fenugreek, garlic, ginger, mustard, poppy seeds, turmeric, mace, nutmeg, curry leaves, white pepper, saffron and aniseeds. The material may contain added starch and edible common salt. The proportion of spices used in the preparation of curry powder shall be not less than 85.0 per cent by weight. The powder shall be free from dirt, mould growth and insect infestation. It shall be free from any added colouring matter and preservatives other than edible common salt. The curry powder shall also conform to the following standards:

Moisture	:	Not more than 14.0 per cent by weight.
Volatile oil	:	Not more than 0.25% (v/w) on dry basis.
Non-volatile ether extract	:	Not less than 7.5% by weight on dry basis.
Edible common salt	:	Not more than 5.0% by weight on dry basis.
Ash insoluble	:	Not more than 2.0% by weight
Crude fibre	:	Not more than 15.0% by weight on dry basis.

Lead : Not more than 10.0 ppm on dry basis.

Whenever edible common salt is added its percentage by weight shall be declared on the label. Also the names of spices contained in the curry powder shall be given on the label in descending order of composition on wt/wt/ basis.

ANISEED OR *SAUNF* IMPORTED

Aniseed or saunf imported means the dried ripe fruit of *Pimpinella anisum*. Foreign edible seeds or matter shall not exceed 5.0 per cent by weight. It shall conform to the following standards:

Total ash	:	Not more than 9% by weight.
Ash insoluble in dilute HCl	:	Not more than 1.5% by weight.
Volatile oil	:	Not less than 1.0% (v/w).

The amount of insect damaged matter shall not exceed 5 per cent by weight.

The term 'insect damaged matter' means spices that are partially or wholly bored by insect.

AJOWAN (BISHOP'S WEED)

Ajowan means the dried ripe seeds of *Trachy spermum* (Linn.) Sprague. The proportion of organic and inorganic extraneous matter shall not exceed 3 per cent and 2 per cent respectively. The seeds shall be free from living insect, insects fragment and rodent contamination visible to the eyes.

Note

(1) The extraneous matter wherever prescribed under this item shall be classified as follows:

(a) Organic extraneous matter such as chaff, stems, straw.

(b) Inorganic extraneous matter such as dust, dirt,

stones and lumps of earth.

(2) Of the permitted extraneous matter in items Caraway, Cardamon, Ammonium, Chillies, Cloves, Coriander, Cemin, Cemin Black, Fennel, Mace, Mustard, Nutmeg, Pepper, Black and Poppy the inorganic extraneous matter shall not exceed 2 per cent by weight.

BEAN

Means dry kidney shaped or flattened seeds of the leaguminous varieties used as food, either whole or prepared as *dall*. It shall not contain hydrocyanic acid exceeding 20 parts per million as determined by A.O.A.C. Maceration method.

PAN MASALA

Pan Masala means the food generally taken as such or in conjunction with Pan, it may contain:-

Betelnut, lime, coconut, catechu, saffron, cardamom, dry fruits, mulethi, sabermusa, other aromatic herbs and spices, sugar, glycerine, glucose, permitted natural colours, menthol and non-prohibited flavours.

It shall be free from added coal tar colouring matter and any other ingredient injurious to health.

It shall also conform to the following standards, namely:-

Total ash	:	Not more than 8.0 percent by weight (on dry basis)
Ash insoluble in dilute hydrocholoric acid	:	Not more than 5.0 percent by weight (on dry basis)

CHAPTER 6

FRUIT PRODUCTS

FRUIT JUICE

The unfermented and unconcentrated liquid expressed from sound, ripe, fresh fruit, and with or without –

(1) Sugar, dextrose, invert sugar, or liquid glucose, either singly or in combination,

(2) Water, peel oil, fruit essences and flavour, common salt, ascorbic acid, citric acid, tartaric acid and malic acid and permitted colours and preservative.

The acidity of the finished product calculated as citric acid shall not be less than 4 per cent in the case of pure lemon juice or pulp and not less than 5 per cent in the case of pure lime juice but shall not exceed 3.5 per cent in the case of other juices.

The total soluble solids for sweetened fruit juice (except tomato juice) shall not be less than 10 per cent.

Fumaric acid may be used up to a maximum limit of 0.5 per cent.

TOMATO JUICE

Canned or bottled, unconcentrated pasteurized juice expressed from tomato with a proportion of the pulp expressed with or without the application of heat by any method that does not add water to such juice, from whole ripe tomatoes from which all stems and objectionable portions have been removed and with or without –

(1) Salt,

(2) Sugar, or dextrose, or both added in dry form,

(3) Citric acid, malic acid or ascorbic acid

(4) Permitted colours

The total soluble solids w/w shall be not less than 5 per cent free of salt.

Fumaric acid may be used up to a maximum limit of 0.5 per cent.

FRUIT SYRUP

Sweetened fruit juice containing sugar, dextrose, invert sugar or liquid glucose either singular or in combination, with or without:

(1) Water, peel-oil fruit essences and flavours, common salt,

(2) Citric acid, ascorbic acid,

(3) Permitted preservative and colours

The total soluble solids w/w shall be not less than 65 per cent.

The minimum percentage of fruit juice in the final product shall be not less than 25.0 per cent w/w

Fumaric acid may be used up to a maximum limit of 0.5 per cent.

FRUIT SQUASH

The expressed juice of the sound, ripe fruit with the pulp, containing sugar, dextrose, invert sugar or liquid glucose either singly or in combination and with or without –

(1) Water, peel-oil fruit essences and flavours, common salt,

(2) Citric acid, ascorbic acid,

(3) Permitted preservative and colours,

The total soluble solids w/w in the finished product shall be not less than 40 per cent.

The minimum percentage of fruit juice in the final product shall be not less than 25.0 per cent w/w.

Fumaric acid may be used up to a maximum limit of 0.5 per cent.

FRUIT BEVERAGE OR FRUIT DRINKS

Any beverage or drink which is purported to be prepared from fruit juice and water or carbonated water, and containing sugar, dextrose, invert sugar or liquid glucose either singly or in combination and with or without –

(1) Water, peel-oil, fruit essences and flavours,

(2) Citric acid, ascorbic acid,

(3) Permitted preservatives and colours.

The total soluble solids w/w in the final product shall be not less than 10 per cent.

The minimum percentage of fruit juice in the final product shall be not less than 5.0 per cent w/w

Fumaric acid may be used up to a maximum limit of 0.5 per cent.

TOMATO SAUCE, TOMATO KETCHUP, TOMATO RELISH OR ANY OTHER EXPRESSION

Conveying the meaning that the product so designated is a form of tomato sauce, shall be a preparation of sound and ripe tomatoes with or without:

(1) Sugar, salt, vinegar, acetic acid, onions, garlic, spices or condiments.

(2) Citric acid, ascorbic acid,

(3) Permitted preservative

The product shall be free from skins and seeds. The product shall show no sign of fermentation when incubated at 37°C for 15 days. The mould count shall not exceed 40 per cent of the fields examined. The yeast and spores shall not exceed 125 per 1/60 c.m.m. The bacterial count shall not exceed 100 million per cc.

Total acidity in terms of acetic acid shall be not less than 1.0 per cent and the total soluble solids w/w not less than 25 per cent. It shall not contain any other vegetable substance.

Fumaric acid may be used up to a maximum limit of 0.5 per cent.

JAM

The product obtained by processing fresh fruit, canned fruit, dried fruit or fruit pulp, with water, sugar, dextrose, invert sugar or liquid glucose either singly or in combination by boiling to a suitable consistency and with or without –

(1) Citric, malic, ascorbic acid,

(2) Permitted preservative and colours

(3) Pectin derived from any fruit

The minimum soluble solids w/w shall be 68 per cent. Jam shall not contain–

(1) Less than 45 per cent of fruit except where fruit is strawberry or raspberry where it shall contain not less than 25 per cent,

(2) Sweetening agent other than specified above,

(3) Apple or rhubarb, but it may contain in any amount that reasonably compensates for any deficiency in the natural acidity or pectin content of the fruit used in its preparation,

(4) Tartaric acid, or

(5) Sagar or gelatin

It shall be free from mould growth. When dry fruit is used, it shall be clearly declared on the label.

Fumaric acid may be used up to a maximum limit of 0.5 per cent.

MARMALADE

The product made from any combination of peel, pulp, and juice of the named citrus fruit by boiling with water, sugar, dextrose, invert sugar, liquid glucose either singly or in combination to a suitable consistency and with or without an acid ingredient in an amount that reasonably compensates for any deficiency in the natural acidity of the fruit used in its preparation, consisting of–

(1) Citric, tartaric, or ascorbic acid,

(2) Lemon or lime juice

It may contain permitted preservatives, colours or pectin derived from any fruit.

It shall not contain less than 45 per cent of the named fruit.

Total soluble solids w/w shall be no less than 65 per cent.

Fumaric acid may be used up to a maximum limit of 0.5 per cent.

FRUIT CHUTNEY

A preparation made from sounds fruits with spices, salt, onion, garlic, sugar, vinegar or acetic acid and shall contain not less than 5.0 per cent of total soluble solid w/w and may contain permitted preservative.

The minimum percentage of fruit in the final product shall not be less than 40.0. The percentage acidity of the product expressed as acetic acid by weight shall be not less than 0.75 and not more than 2.0 The ash content shall not exceed 5.0 per cent.

SAUCE

Shall be the product derived from any suitable kind and variety of fruity and vegetable which are wholesome and which shall be practically free from insect of fungal attack or blemish affecting the quality of the fruit or vegetable. The only substances that may be added are fruit, vegetable their pulp, juice, dried fruit, sugar, spices, salt, vinegar, acetic acid, citric acid, malic, acid, onion, garlic, flavouring material and permitted preservatives. It shall not contain any coal tar dye.

Fumaric acid may be used up to a maximum limit of 0.5%.

The minimum total soluble solids shall not be less, than 15 per cent. The total acidity in terms of acetic acid shall not be less than 1.0 per cent.

CHAPTER 7

CEREALS

ATTA

The coarse product obtained by milling or grinding wheat. It shall conform to the following standards:

Moisture	:	Not more than 14.0 per cent (when determined by heating at 130-133°C
Total ash	:	Not more than 2.0 per cent (on weight basis).
Ash insoluble in dilute HCl	:	Not more than 0.15 per cent (on dry weight basis).
Gluten (on dry weight basis)	:	Not less than 6.0 per cent
Alcoholic acidity (with 90 per cent alcohol) expressed as H_2SO_4 (on dry weight basis)	:	Not more than 0.18 per cent).

Rodent hair and excreta shall not exceed [2] pieces per kg.

FORTIFIED *ATTA*

The product obtained by adding one or more of the following materials to *atta*, namely –

(1) Calcium carbonate (prepared chalk popularly known as *Creta preparata*).

(2) Iron,

(3) Thiamine,

(4) Riboflavin, and

(5) Niacin

The calcium carbonate powder, if added for fortification shall be in such amount that 100 parts by weight for fortified atta shall contain not less than 0.30 and not more than 0.35 parts by weight of calcium carbonate.

PROTEIN RICH (*PAUSTIK*) *ATTA*

The product obtained by mixing groundnut flour up to an extent of 10.0 per cent. IT shall be free insect or fungus infestation, odour and rancid taste. It shall not contain added flavouring and colouring and agents or any other extraneous matter. It shall conform to the following standards:

Moisture	:	Not more than 14.0% on dry basis.
Total ash	:	Not more than 2.75%
Ash insoluble in dilute HCl	:	Not more than 0.1% on dry basis.
Total protein (N_x 6.25) on Dry basis	:	Not more than 12.5% on dry basis.
Crude fibre	:	Not more than 2.5% by dry basis.
Alcoholic acidity (with 90 per cent alcohol expressed as H_2SO_4)	:	Not more than 0.12%

MAIDA (WHEAT FLOUR)

The fine product made by milling or grinding wheat and bolting or dressing the resulting wheat meal. It shall conform to the following standards:

Moisture	:	Not more than 14.8% (when determined by heating at 130-133°C for 2 hours).
Total ash (on dry weight basis)	:	Not more than 1.0%
Ash insoluble in dilute HCl (on dry weight basis)	:	Not more than 0.1 per cent.
Gluten (on dry weight basis)	:	Not less than 7.5%
Alcoholic acidity (with 90 per cent alcohol) expressed as H_2SO_4 (on dry weight basis)	:	Not less than 0.12%

Rodent hair and excreta shall not exceed 5 pieces per kg.

If the product is to be used for bakery purposes, the following flour-treatment agents in the quantities mentioned against each may be used, namely –

Benzoyl peroxide (max)	:	40 p.p.m.
Potassium bromate (max)	:	20 p.p.m.
Ascorbic acid (max)	:	200 p.p.m.

FORTIFIED *MAIDA*

The product obtained by adding one or more of the following materials to *maida*, namely –

(1) Calcium carbonate (prepared chalk popularly known as Creta preparata)

(2) Iron,

(3) Riboflavin, and

(4) Nicacie.

The calcium carbonate powder, if added for fortification shall be in such amount that 100 parts by weight of fortified *maida* shall contain not less than 0.30 and not more than 0.35 parts by weight of calcium carbonate.

PROTEIN RICH (PAUSHTIK) *MAIDA*

The product obtained by mixing *maida* (wheat flour) with groundnut flour up to an extent of 10.0 per cent. It shall be free from insect or fungus infestation, odour and rancid taste. It shall not contain added flavouring and colouring agents or any other extraneous matter. It shall conform to the following standards:

Moisture	:	Not more than 14.0%
Total ash	:	Not more than 1.4%
Ash insoluble in dilute HCl	:	Not more than 0.1% on dry basis
Total protein (N_x 6.25)	:	Not less than 12.5% on dry basis
Crude fibre	:	Not more than 0.53% on dry basis.
Alcoholic acidity (with 90 per cent alcohol) expressed as H_2SO_4	:	Not more than 0.12%
Gulten	:	Not less than 7.0% on dry basis

SEMOILAN (*SUJI OR RAWA*)

The product prepared from wheat by process of grinding and bolting. It shall be free from musty smell and off-odour and shall be creamy yellow in colour. It shall conform to the following standards:

Moisture	:	Not more than 14.5 per cent (when determined by heating at 130-133°C for 2 hours).
Total ash (on dry weight basis)	:	Not more than 1.0%
Ash insoluble in dilute HCl (on dry weight basis)	:	Not more than 0.1%

Gluten (on dry weight basis) : Not less than 6.0%

Alcoholic acidity
(with 90 per cent alcohol)
expressed as H_2SO_4
(on dry weight basis) : Not more than 0.18%

Rodent hair and excreta shall not exceed 5 pieces per kg.

BESAN

The *besan* obtained by grinding dehuked Bengal gram (*Cicer arietinum*) and shall not contain any added colouring matter or any other foreign ingredients. Besan confirm to following standards:

Total ash : Not more than 5 percent

Ash insoluble in HCl : Not more than 0.5 percent

PEARL BARLEY

Shall be the product obtained from sound and clean barley. It shall be whitest in colour and shall be free from fermented, musty on other objectionable taste or colour, adulterants, insect, fungus infestation and rodent contamination. It shall not contain other food-grain more than one per cent by weight.

Barley powder shall also conform to the following standards, namely –

Total ash (on dry basis) : Not mention 1%

Ash insoluble in dilute
hydrochloric acid (on dry basis) : Not more than 0.1%

Crude fibre (on dry basis) : Not more than 0.5%

Alcoholic acidity : Not more than 0.10% as H_2SO_4 with 90% alcohol

WHOLE WHEAT BARLEY POWDER

The product obtained by grinding clean and sound dehusked barley grains. It shall conform to the following standards:

Moisture	:	Not more from 14.0% (when determined by heating of 130° for two hours)
Total ash (on dry weight basis)	:	Not more than 3.0%
Ash insoluble in dilute HCl with (on dry weight basis)	:	Not more 0.5%
Alcoholic acidity (with 90% alcohol) expressed on H_2SO_4 (on dry weight basis)	:	Not more than 0.17%

Rodent hair and excreta shall not exceed 5 per cent per kg.

FOOD GRAINS

Food grains meant for human consumption shall be whole or broken kernels of cereals, millets and pulses. Paddy is included in food grains and shall have different units for refractions whenever specified.

Food grains meant for human consumption shall conform to the following standards:

(1) **General** – Food grains shall be free for deleterious material including artificial colouring material. The pesticide residue, if any, shall not exceed the prescribed permissible unit. Bajra and wheat shall not contain ergot affected grains more than 0.05 per cent by weight.

(2) **Foreign Material** – Foreign matters means any extraneous matter other than food grain and will comprise inorganic water. Inorganic water which includes sand, gravel, disrt, peddebs, stones, lumps of earth, clay and mud shall not exceed one per cent whereas in case of paddy, it shall not exceed 3 per cent by weight. Organic matter which includes chalf, straw, weed seeds, inedible grain, oil seeds and other non-poisonous seeds shall not exceed 3 per cent by weight.

(3) **Damaged Grain** – Damaged grain means damaged by fungus, moisture or heating and wherein the damage is not superficial but the grain is affected internally it shall not exceed 5 per cent by weight.

(4) **Insect Damage** – The amount of weevilled grains (by count) shall not be more than 10 per cent or uric acid. Content, arising as a result of insect damaged shall not exceed 10 per cent milligrams's per 100 grammes, whichever is lower.

(5) **Rodent Hair and Excreta** – Rodent hair and excreta . shall not exceed 5 percent per kg of the sample.

(6) **Moisture** – The lose in weight by heating the purchased food grains at 130°C – 133°C for two hours shall not exceed 16 per cent.

The words 'cereals' and 'food grains' should be given an extended meaning so as to include the seed of both gramminaceal and seguminosal, that is to say, both cereals strictly so-called and pulses which are not strictly "cereal" as understood by a botanist:

(1) *Matar daal* was treated by the Public Analyst as 'Pulse' and he reported the sample to be adulterated. The court took *matar daal* as "food grain". The accused was acquitted by the court for non-performance of additional tests. Held that the decision of the trying court could not be assailed and that the absence of evidence about it being "food grain" was immaterial.

(2) *Matar Daal* – Analyst treating it as a pulse and reporting the sample to be adulterated – Court taking it also to be 'food grain' – Accused acquitted for non-performance of additional tests under A.18.06(i) and (ii).

Biscuits, other than wafer biscuits shall be made from *maida*, *vanaspati*, or refined edible oil or table butter or *deshi* butter or margarine, or *ghee*, or other mixture. It may contain edible common salt. It may contain any one or more of the following ingredients, namely:

Permitted anti-oxidants; Emulsifying and stabilizing agents; Permitted preservatives Baking powder; Butter milk End colours; Powder; Cereals; Cheese; Chocolate; Citric acid; Cocoa; Edible desiccated coconut; Dextrose; Dry fruits and nuts, eggs; Enzymes; Permitted flavouring agents; Flavour improvers and fixers; Flour improvers; Ginger; Groundnut cake flour; Milk products; Honey; Jellifying agents; Liquid glucose; Malt products; Oilseeds; Spices; Sugar and sugar products; Edible starches, such as potato Invert sugar; Starch; Jaggery; Wheat atta and yeast; Gluten.

Biscuits shall conform to the following standards, namely:

(1) Ash insoluble in the dilute hydrochloric acid (on dry basis) shall not be more than 1.5 per cent;

(2) Alcoholic (90 per cent alcohol) acidity of extracted fat (as oleic acid) shall not exceed 1.5 per cent.

CORNFLOUR (MAIZE STARCH)

The starch obtained from maize (*Zea mays* L.). It shall contain no added colour, flavours or other chemicals. It shall be free from dirt, insects, larvae and impurities or other extraneous matter.

It shall conform to the following standards:

Moisture	:	Not more than 12.5 per cent
Total Ash	:	Not more than 0.5 per cent on dry basis
Ash insoluble in dilute HCl	:	Not more than 0.1 per cent on dry basis

Alcohol acidity (with 90 per cent alcohol)	:	Shall be equivalent to not more than 2.0 ml. N Na OH per 100 g. of dried starch.

CORN FLAKES

The product obtained from dehulled, degermed and cook corn (*Zea mays* L) by flaking, partially drying and toasting. It shall be in the form of crisp flakes or reasonably uniform size and golden brown in colour. It shall be free from dirt, insects, larvae and impurities and any other extraneous matter.

It shall conform to the following standards:

Moisture	:	Not more than 7.5 per cent
Total ash excluding Salt	:	Not more than 1.0 per cent on dry basis
Ash insoluble in dilute HCl	:	Not more than 0.1 per cent on dry basis
Alcoholic acidity with 90 per cent alcohol	:	Shall be equivalent to not more than 2.0 ml of N NaOH per 100 g of dried substance

CUSTARD POWDER

The products obtained from maize (*Zea mays* L.) or sago/ tapioca with or without the addition of small quantities of edible starches obtained from arrowroot, potato or *jawar* (*Sorghum vulgare*) and with or without the addition of edible common salt, milk and albuminous matter. It may contain permitted colours and flavours. It shall be free from any other foreign matter. It shall be in the from of the fine powder, free from rancidity, fermented and musty odour.

It shall conform to the following standards, namely:

Moisture	:	Not more than 12.5%
Total ash excluding added common salt (on dry basis)	:	Not more than 0.5%

Ash insoluble in hydrochloric acid (on dry-basis)	:	Not less than 0.1%

MACARONI PRODUCTS (MACARONI, SPAGHETTI, VERMICELLI)

The marcaroni products obtained from *suji* or *maida* with or without addition of ingredients like edible groundnut flour, tapioca flour, soya flour, milk powder, spices, vitamins, minerals, by kneading the dough and extending it. It shall be free from added colour, dirt, insects, larvae and impurities or any other extraneous matter.

It shall conform to the following standards:

Moisture	:	Not more than 12.5%
Total ash	:	Not more than 1.0% on dry basis
Ash insoluble in dilute HCl	:	Not more than 0.1% on dry basis
Nitrogen	:	Not less than 1.7% on dry basis

MALTED MILK FOOD

The product obtained by mixing whole milk or partially skimmed milk or milk powder with malt extract and cereal grain flour in such a manner as to secure complete hydrolysis of the starchy material. It shall not contain added sugars, foreign fat and preservatives. It may contain cocoa powder add natural colouring matter. Malted milk food shall be in the form of powder.

It shall conform of the following standards:

Moisture	:	Not more than 5.0%
Total ash	:	Not more than 5.0% on dry basis
Ash insoluble in dilute HCl	:	Not less than 0.1% on dry basis
Milk fat	:	Not less than 7.0% on dry basis

Nitrogen	:	Not less than 1.0% on dry basis
Solubility per cent	:	Not less than 80.0%
Starch	:	1 g. dissolved in 5 ml. of boiling water, cooled and treated with 0.5 ml. of 0.05 per cent iodine solution in KI does not develop any blue colour
Bacterial count	:	Not more than 50,000 per g.
Coliform count	:	Not more than 10 per g.

The nitrogen content shall not be less than 1.8 per cent on dry basis, if the malted milk food contains cocoa.

ROLLED OATS (QUICK-COOKING OATS)

The product made from sound hulled oats (Avena sativa). It shall be free from added colours, rancidity and flavouring agents. It shall be in from of thin flakes of uniform size having a light cream colour. It shall be free from dirt, insects fragments.

It shall conform to the following standards:

Moisture	:	Not more than 10.0%
Total ash	:	Not more than 2.0%on dry basis
Ash insoluble in dilute HCl	:	Not more than 0.1 % on dry basis
Nitrogen	:	Not less than 1.8% on dry basis
Crude fibre	:	Not more than 2.0% on dry basis
Alcoholic acidity (with 90 per cent alcohol)	:	Shall be equivalent to not more than 8.0 ml. N NaOH per 100g of dried substance.

BREAD – WHEAT – MEAL BREAD (BROWN BREAD) AND WHITE BREAD

The products prepared from a mixture of wheat *atta*, *maida*, water, salt, yeast or other fermentative medium. It may also contain one or more of the following ingredients, namely, condensed milk, milk powder (whole or skimmed), whey and curd, gluten, sugar, honey, liquid glucose, malt product, edible starches, edible groundnut flour, edible soya flour, *vanaspati* or refined edible oil of suitable type of butter or *ghee* or their mixture, lecithin, glycerine, glyceryl monostearate, albumin, lime water lysine and sorbitol.

It may contain the improvers given below:

Ammonium persulphate	:	Not more than 0.25%
Calcium phosphate	:	Not more than 0.25%
Calcium carbonate	:	Not more than 0.5%
Potassium bromate	:	Not more than 0.005%
Sodium stearoyl	:	2 lactylate;
Calcium stearoyl (singly or in combination)	·	2 alctylate. Not more than 0.5%

It may contain one or more of the following mould inhibitors:

Calcium or sodium propionate	:	Not more than 0.5%
Sorbic acid or its sodium, potassium or calcium salts	:	Not more than 0.1%
Acetic acid or lactic acid	:	Not more than 0.25%
Vinegar	:	Not more than 0.5%
Acid calcium phosphate	:	Not more than 1.0%
Sodium diacetate	:	Not more than 0.4%
Acid sodium pyrophosphate	:	Not more than 0.5%

It shall be free from dirt, insects and insect fragments, larvae, rodent hairs and maggots. It shall be free from added colouring matter. It shall conform to the following standards:

Alcoholic acidity (with 90 % Alcohol)	:	Shall be not more than the equivalent of 7.5 ml. N NaOH per 100 g. of dried substance.
Ash insoluble in dilute HCl On dry basis Crude fibre on dry weight basis	:	Not more than 0.1%
What-meal bread	:	Not more than 1.8% (brown bread)
White bread	:	Not more than 0.5%

CHAPTER 8

COMMON SALT, EDIBLE OILS AND FATS

SALT

Iodised salt is crystalline solid, white or pale, pink or light grey in colour, free from visible contamination with clay, grit and other extraneous adulterants and impurities. It shall not contain moisture in excess of 6.0 per cent of the weight of the undried sample. It shall contain on dry weight basis (a) at least 96.0 per cent by weight of sodium chloride (NaCl), (b) not more than 1.0 per cent by weight matter insoluble in water, (c) not more than 3.0 per cent by weight of matter soluble in water other sodium chloride, and (d) one part to 40,000 parts (25 ppm) by weight of potassium iodate or one part to 50,000 parts (20 ppm) by weight of potassium iodide or equivalent iodine.

The sodium chloride content (as NaCl) and the matter soluble in water other than sodium chloride on dry weight basis shall be specified in columns (2) and (3) of Table 8.1 against the period of validity mentioned in the corresponding entry in column (1) of the table. The matter insoluble in water shall not exceed 1.0 per cent by weight on dry weight basis:

Provided that table salt may contain aluminium silicate on an anti-packing agent to a maximum extent of 2.0 per cent:

Provided further that the total matter insoluble in water in such cases shall not exceed 2.2 per cent and the sodium chloride content on dry basis shall not be less than 97.0 per cent by weight.

Table 8.1: Period of validity, Percentage of Sodium Chloride and Soluble Matter

Period of Validity	Minimum percentage of Sodium Chloride content as NaCI (on dry basis)	Minimum percentage of matter soluble in water other from sodium Chloride (on dry basis)
Up to 31-3.82	94.0	5.0
from 1.4.82 to 31.3.83	94.5	4.5
from 1.4.83 to 31.3.84	95.0	4.0
from 1.4.84 to 31.3.85	95.5	3.5
from 1.4.85 on wards	96.0	3.0

EDIBLE OILS

COCONUT OIL (*NARYAL KA TEL*)

The oil expressed from copra obtained from the kernel of *Cocos mucifera* nuts. It shall be clear and free from rancidity, suspended or other foreign matter, separated water, added colouring or flavouring substances, or mineral oil. It shall conform to the following standards:

Butyro refractometer reading at 40°C	:	34.0 to 35.5
Saponification value	:	Not less than 250
Iodine value	:	7.5 to 10.0
Polenske value	:	Not less than 13.0
Free fatty acid as Oleic acid	:	Not more than 3.0%

COTTON SEED OIL (*BINOLA KA TEL*)

The oil expressed from clean, sound and decorticated cotton seeds (genus *Gossypium*, refined and dehydrated. It shall be clear, free from rancidity, suspended or other foreign matter, separated or other foreign matter, separated water, added colouring or flavouring substances, or mineral oil. It shall conform to the following standards:

Butyro refractometer reading at 40°C	:	55.6 to 60.2
Saponification value	:	190 to 198
Iodine value	:	98 to 112
Unsaponifiable matter	:	Not more than 1.5%
Free fatty acid as Oleic acid	:	Not more than 1.0%

There shall be no turbidity after keeping the filtered sample at 30°C for 24 hours.

GROUNDNUT OIL (*MOONGH-PHALI-KA-TEL*)

The oil expressed from clean and sound groundnuts (*Arachis hypogoes*) shall be clear, free from rancidity, suspended or other foreign matter, separated water, added colouring or flavouring substances, or mineral oil. It shall conform to the following standards:

Butyro refractometer reading at 40°C	:	54.0 to 57.1
Saponification value	:	188 to 196
Iodine value	:	85 to 99
Unsaponifiable matter	:	Not more than 1.0 %
Free fatty acid as Oleic acid	:	Not more than 3.0%
Bellier test (Turbidity temperature - acetic acid method)	:	30°C to 41°C

MAHUA OIL

The oil expressed from clean and sound seeds or nuts of Madhuca (*Bassia latifolia* or *B. longifolia* or a mixture of both). It shall be clear and shall be free from rancidity, suspended or other foreign matter, separated water, added colouring flavouring substances, or mineral oil. It shall be refined and shall conform to the following standards:

Butyro refractometer reading at 40°C	:	49.5 to 52.7
Saponification value	:	187 to 196
Iodine value	:	58 to 70
Unsaponifiable matter	:	Not more than 2.0 %
Free fatty acid as Oleic acid	:	Not more than 0.25%

RAPE-SEED OIL (*TORIA OIL*) MUSTARD OIL (*SARSON-KA-TEL*)

The oil expressed from clean and sound mustard seeds, belonging to the compestris, juncea or napus varieties of Brassica. It shall be clear, free from rancidity, suspended or foreign matter, separated water, added colouring or flavouring substances or mineral oil. It shall conform to the following standards:

Butyro refractometer reading at 40°C	:	58.0 to 60.5
Saponification value	:	168 to 177
Iodine value	:	96 to 100: Polybromide test shall Be negative
Unsaponifiable matter	:	Not more than 1.0% by weight
Free fatty acid as Oleic acid	:	Not more than 3.0%
Bellier test (Turbidity temperature - acetic acid method)	:	Not more than 27.5°C
Test for argemone oil	:	Negative
Test for Hydrocyanic acid	:	Negative

LINSEED OIL (*TISI KA TEL*)

The oil obtained by process of expressing clean and sound linseed (*Linum usitatissimum*). It shall be clear, free from rancidity, suspended or other foreign matter, separated water, added colouring or flavouring substances, or mineral oil. It shall conform to the following standards:

Butyro refractometer reading at 40°C	:	69.5 to 74.3
Saponification value	:	188 to 195
Iodine value	:	Not less than 170
Unsaponifiable matter	:	Not more than 1.5%
Free fatty acid as Oleic acid	:	Not more than 2.0%
Bellier test (Turbidity temperature - acetic acid method)	:	Not more than 27.5°C

OLIVE OIL

The oil expressed from the ripe olive fruit (*Olea europea*). It shall be clear, free from rancidity, suspended or other foreign matter, separated water, added colouring or flavouring substances or mineral oil. It shall conform to the following standards:

Butyro refractometer reading at 40°C	:	53.0 to 56.0
Saponification value	:	185 to 196
Iodine value	:	79 to 90
Unsaponifiable matter	:	Not more than 1.0%
Free fatty acid as Oleic acid	:	Not more than 3.0%

POPPY SEED OIL

The oil expressed from poppy seeds (*Papaver somniferum*). It shall be clear, free from rancidity, suspended or other foreign matter, separated water, added colouring or flavouring substances, or mineral oil. It shall conform to the following standards:

Butyro refractometer reading at 40°C	:	63.0 to 64.0
Saponification value	:	186 to 194

Iodine value	:	133 to 143
Unsaponifiable matter	:	Not more than 1.0%
Free fatty acid as Oleic acid	:	Not more than 3.0%

SAFFLOWERS OIL (*BARREY KA TEL*)

The oil expressed from the seeds of *Carthamus tinctorius*. It shall be clear, free from rancidity, suspended or other foreign matter, separated water, added colouring or flavouring substances, or mineral oil. It shall conform to the following standards:

Butyro refractometer reading at 40°C	:	62.0 to 64.7
Saponification value	:	186 to 196
Iodine value	:	135 to 146
Unsaponifiable matter	:	Not more than 1.0 %
Free fatty acid as Oleic acid	:	Not more than 3.0%
Bellier test (Turbidity temperature – Acetic acid method)	:	Not more than 16°C

TARAMIRA OIL

The oil expressed from clean and sound seeds of (*Eruca sativa*). It shall be clear, free from rancidity, suspended or other foreign matter, separated water, added colouring or flavouring substances, or mineral oil. It shall conform to the following standards:

Butyro refractometer reading at 40°C	58.0 to 60.0
Saponification value	174 to 177
Iodine value	99 to 146
Unsaponifiable matter	Not more than 1.0 %
Free fatty acid as Oleic acid	Not more than 3.0%

TIL OIL (*GINGELLY OR SESAME OIL*)

The oil expressed from clean and sound seeds of *Til* (*Sesaamum indicum*), black, brown, white, or mixed. It shall be clear, free from rancidity, suspended or other foreign matter, separated water, added colouring or flavouring substances, or mineral oil. It shall conform to the following standards:

Butyro refractometer reading at 40°C	:	58.0 to 61.0
Saponification value	:	188 to 193
Iodine value	:	105 to 115
Unsaponifiable matter	:	Not more than 1.5 %
Free fatty acid as Oleic acid	:	Not more than 3.0%
Bellier test (Turbidity temperature Acetic acid method)	:	Not more than 22°C

Provided that the oil obtained from white sesame seeds grown in Tripura, Assam and West Bengal shall conform to the following standards:

Butyro refractometer reading at 40°C	:	60.5 to 61.0
Saponification value	:	185 to 190
Iodine value	:	115 to 120
Unsaponifiable matter	:	Not more than 3.0 %
Free fatty acid as Oleic acid	:	Not more than 2.5%
Bellier test (Turbidity temperature Acetic acid method	:	Not more than 22°C

NIGER SEED OIL (*SARGIYA KA TEL*)

The edible oil obtained by process of expressing clean and solid seeds of *Guizotia abyssinica*. It shall be clear and free from rancidity, suspended or other foreign matter, separated water, added-colouring or flavouring substances, mineral or other oil. It shall conform to the following standards:

Butyro refractometer reading at 40°C	:	61.0 to 65.0
Saponification value	:	188 to 193
Iodine value	:	125 to 135

Unsaponifiable matter	:	Not more than 1.0 %
Free fatty acid as Oleic acid	:	Not more than 3.0%
Bellier test (Turbidity temperature Acetic acid method)	:	22°C to 27°C

SOYABEAN OIL

The oil expressed from clean and sound soyabeans (*Soja max*) from which the major portion of the gums naturally present have been removed by hydration and mechanical or physical separation. It shall be clear, free from rancidity, suspended or other foreign matter, separated water, added colouring or flavouring substances or mineral oil.

It shall conform to the following standards:

Butyro refractometer reading at 40°C	:	61.7 to 69.5
Saponification value	:	189 to 195
Iodine value	:	120 to 141
Unsaponifiable matter	:	Not more than 1.5 %
Free fatty acid as Oleic acid	:	Not more than 1.25%
Phosphorus	:	Not more than 0.02%

MAIZE (CORN) OIL

The oil, extracted from the gram of clean and sound seed of *Zea mays* Linn, *Fam Granniae*, refined. It shall be free from rancidity, suspended or other foreign matter separated water, added colouring or flavouring substances or mineral oil. It shall conform to the following standards:

Butyro refractometer reading at 40°C	:	57.7 to 62.5
Saponification value	:	187 to 195
Iodine value	:	103 to 128
Unsaponifiable matter	:	Not more than 1.5%
Free fatty acid as Oleic acid	:	Not more than 1.0%

REFINED VEGETABLE OIL

Any edible vegetable oil which is obtained by expression, neutralized with alkali, bleached with absorbent earth and/or activated carbon and deodorized with steam. No other chemical agent shall be used. The name of the vegetable oil from which the refined oil has been manufactured shall be clearly specified on the label of the container. In addition to the under-mentioned standards to which refined vegetable oils shall conform, the standards prescribed in these rules the specified edible oil shall also apply except for free fatty acid content, which shall be not more than 0.25 per cent. Moisture shall not exceed 0.10 per cent by weight.

ALMOND OIL

The oil expressed from the seeds of *Prunus amygdalus* Batach, var. *dulcis* Koehne (sweet almond) or of *Prunus amygdalus* Batach, var. *Amara focke* (bitter almond), without the application of heat. It shall be clear, free from rancidity, suspended or other foreign matter, separated water, added colouring or flavouring substance or mineral oil. It shall conform to the following standards:

Butyro refractometer reading at 40°C	:	55 to 57
Saponification value	:	186 to 195
Iodine value	:	90 to 109
Unsaponifiable matter	:	Not more than 3.0%
Free fatty acid as Oleic acid	:	Not more than 60°C

WATER-MELON SEED OIL

The oil extracted from clean, sound seeds of the fruit of Water-Melon (*Citrullus vulgaris* Schrad) (Family: *cucurbitaceae*). It shall be clear, free from rancidity, adulterants, sediments, suspended and other foreign matter, separated water, added colouring and flavouring substances and mineral Oil. It shall conform to the following standards:

Moisture and insoluble matter	:	Not more 0.25%
Butyro refractometer reading at 40°C	:	55.6 to 61.7
Saponification value	:	190 to 198
Iodine value	:	115 to 125
Free fatty acid as Oleic acid	:	Not more than 3.0%
Unsaponifiable matter	:	Not more than 1.5%

MARAGARINE

Maragarine an emulsion of edible oils and fats with water. It shall be free from rancidity, added colouring and flavouring substances, mineral oil and animal body fats. It may contain common salt not exceeding 2.5 per cent, permitted emulsifying and stabilizing agents and butylated-hydroxyanisole (BHA) up to a maximum limit of 0.02 per cent. It shall conform to the following specifications, namely:

Fat	:	Not less than 80 per cent mass/mass.
Moisture	:	Not less than 12 per cent and not more than 16 per cent mass/mass
Vitamin A	:	Not less than 30 I. U. per gram of the product at the time of sale.

It shall contain not less than 5 per cent of its weight of Til oil but sufficient to ensure that when separated fat is mixed with refined groundnut oil in the proportion of 20:80, the red colour produced by the Baudouin test shall not be lighter than 2 red units in 1 cm. cell on a Lovibond scale.

Note: - The oils to be used in the manufacture to margarine shall be the same as used in the manufacture of *vanaspati* specified in the Vegetable Oil Products Control Order, 1947.

EDIBLE FAT

Beef Fat or Suet

Fat obtained from a beef carcass. It shall have a saponification value carrying from 193 to 200 and an Iodine value from 35 to 46.

Mutton fat means fat obtained from the carcass of sheep. It shall have a Saponification value carrying from 192 to 195 and an Iodine value from 35 to 46.

Goat Fat

The fat rendered from goat. It shall have a Saponification value varying from 193 to 196 and an Iodine value from 36 to 45.

Lard

The fat rendered from hogs and shall not contain more than one per cent of substances other than fatty acids and fat. It shall have a saponification value carrying from 192 to 198 and Iodine value from 52 to 65.

Cocoa Butter

The fat obtained by expression from the nibs of the beans of *Theobroma cocoa* L. It shall be free from other oils and fats, mineral oil and added colours.

It shall conform to the following standards:

Percentage of free fatty acids	:	(calculated as not more than 1.5 oleic acid)
Iodine value	:	32 to 42.
Melting point	:	29°C to 34°C.
Butyrorefractometer reading at 40°C	:	40.9 to 48.0
Saponification value	:	185 to 200

Low and High Fat Cocoa Powder

The powder which is the partially defatted product derived from the cocoa bean, the seed of *Theobroma cocoa* L. It may be subjected to treatments during manufacture with alkali and/ or magnesium carbonate, bicarbonate, and with tartaric, citric or phosphoric acids. It shall be free from rancidity, dirt, filth, insects and insect fragments or fungus, infestations.

It shall conform to the following standards:

Total ash	:	Not more than 14.0 per cent (on moisture and fat free basis)
Ash insoluble in dilute HCl	:	Not more than 1.0 per cent (on moisture fat free basis)
Alkalinity of total ash	:	Not more than 6.0 per cent as K_2O (on moisture and fat free basis).

Cocoa Butter

For low fat	:	Not less than 10.0 per cent (on moisture and fat free basis);
For high fat	:	Not less than 20 per cent (on moisture and fat free basis).

FAT SPREAD

Fat Spread means a product in the form of water in oil emulsion, or an aqeuous phase and a fat phase of edible oils and fats excluding animal body fats. The individual oil and fat used in the spread shall conform to the respective standards prescribed by these rules.

Fat spread shall be classified into the following three groups:

Milk fat spread	:	Fat content will be exclusively milk fat.
Mixed for spread	:	Fat content will be a mixture of milk fat with any one or more of hydrogenated, unhydorgenated refined edible vegetable oils or interesterified fat.
Vegetable fat spread	:	Fat content will be a mixture of any two or more of hydrogenated, unhydrogenated, refined vegetable oil or interesterfied fat.

The fact content shall be declared on the label. In mixed fat spread, the milk fat content shall also be declared on the label along with the total fat content.

The word 'butter' will not be associated while labelling the product.

It may contained edible common salt not exceeding 2 percent by weigh in aqueous phase; milk solids-not-fat; lactic acid, butyric acid, valeric acid, cinnamon oil, and Ethyl butyrate may also be added as flavouring agent upto 0.08 percent m/ml, Diacetyl may be added as flavouring agents not exceeding 4.0 p.p.m., permitted emulsifier and stabilizers' permitted antioxidants (BHA or TBHQ) not exceeding 0.02 percent of the fat content of the spread; permitted Class II preservatives namely sorbic acid including its sodium, potassium salts (calculated as benzoic acid) or benzoic acid and its sodium and potassium salts (calculated as benzoic acid) singly or in combination not exceeding 1000 parts per million by weight; and sequenstering agents. It may contain annatto and/ or carotene as colouring agents. It shall be free from animal body fat, mineral oil and wax. Vegetable fat spread shall contain raw or refined Sesame oil (Til oil) in sufficient quantity so that when separated fat is mixed with refined groundnut oil in the proportion of 20:80 the red colour produced by Baudouin test shall not be lighter than 2.5 red units in 1 cm. Cell on a Lovibond scale.

It shall also conform to the following standards, namely:-

Fat	: Not more than 80 percent and not less than 40 percent by weight.
Moisture	: Not more than 56 percent and not less than 16 percent by weight.
Melting of Extracted fat (capacity slip method) in case of vegetable fat spread	: Note more than 37 deg C.

Unsaponifiable matter of extracted fat -

(a) In case of milk and fat and mixed fat spread	: Not more than 1 percent by weight.
(b) In case of vegetable for spread	: Not more than 1.5 percent
(c) Acid value of extracted fat	: Not more than 0.5.

It shall be compulsorily sold in spread packages weighing not more than 500 g. under Agmark Certification Mark.

1. The vegetable fat spread shall contain not less than 25 IU syntheic vitamin 'A' per gram at the time of packing and shall show a positive test for vitamin 'A' when tested by Antimony Trichloride (Carr-Price) reagengs (as per I.S. 5886-1970).
2. It shall contain starch not less than 100 PPM and not more than 150 PPM.

CHAPTER 9

BAKING POWDER AND STARCHY FOODS

BAKING POWDER

Means a combination capable, under conditions of baking, of yielding, carbon dioxide, and consists of sodium bicarbonate, and acid-reacting material, starch or other neutral material.

The acid-reacting material of baking powder shall be –

(1) Tartaric acid or its salts, or both,

(2) Acid salts of phosphoric acid, or

(3) Acid compounds of aluminium, or

(4) Any combination of the foregoing.

When tested, baking powder shall yield not less than 10 per cent of its weight of carbon dioxide.

STARCHY FOODS

Arrowroot

Means the separated and purified starch from the rhizomes of the plants known as *Muranta arundinaceaor* from *Curcumaaugustifolia*.

Sago shall mean small hard globules or pearls made from either the starch of the Sago palm or the tubers of tapioca

(*Manihot utilissima*) and shall be free from any extraneous matter including natural colours.

It shall conform to the following standards, namely –

(1) Total ash (on dry basis) shall not be more than 0.4 per cent;

(2) Ash insoluble in dilute hydrochloric acid (on dry basis) shall not exceed 0.1 per cent.

Asafoetida (*Hing* or *Hingra*)

Means the oleo-gumresin obtained from the rhizome and roots of *Ferula alliaces*, *Ferula rubricaulis* and other species of Ferula. It shall not contain any olophony resin) galbanum resin, ammoniaccum-resin, or any other foreign resin. Hing shall conform to the following standards, namely:

(1) Total ash content shall not exceed 15 per cent by weight.

(2) Ash insoluble in dilute hydrochloric acid shall not exceed 2.5 per cent by weight.

(3) The alcoholic extract (with 90 per cent alcohol) shall not be less than 12 per cent as estimated by the USP 1936 method.

(3) Starch shall not exceed 1 per cent by weight.

Hingra shall conform to the following standards, namely:

(1) The total ash content shall not exceed 20 per cent by weight.

(2) Ash insoluble in dilute hydrochloric acid shall not exceed 8 per cent by weight.

(3) The alcoholic extract (with 90 per cent alcohol) shall not be less than 50 per cent as estimated by USP 1936 method.

(4) Starch shall not exceed one per cent by weight.

Compounded asafoetida or *Bandhani Hing* is composed of one or more varieties of asafotida (*Irani* or *Pathani* Hing or both) and gum Arabic, edible starches or edible cereal flour.

It shall not contain:

(1) Colopony resin,

(2) Galbanum resin,

(3) Ammoniaccum-resin,

(4) Any other foreign resin,

(5) Coal tar dyes,

(6) Mineral pigment,

(7) More than 10 per cent total ash content,

(8) More than 1.5 per cent ash insoluble in dilute hydrochloric acid,

(9) Less than 5 per cent alcoholic extract, (with 90 per cent of alcohol) as estimated by the USP 1936 method.

CHAPTER 10

SWEETENING AGENTS

CANE SUGAR

Cane Sugar is the crystallized sugar obtained from sugarcane beet-root, etc., and includes the refined product obtained from *gur*.

It shall contain not more than 0.7 per cent of ash, not more than 1.5 per cent of water and not less than 96.5 per cent of sucrose.

It may contain sulphur dioxide in concentration not exceeding 70 parts per million.

MISRI (PALM AND SUGARCANE)

Misri shall be the crystallized sugar having sucrose not less than 98.0% and total ash not more than 0.4%.

REFINED SUGAR

Means the sugar obtained from the juice of sugarcane or Sugar-Beet. It shall be crystalline, white or colourless, free from dirt and other extraneous matter. It shall conform to the following standards:

Sucrose	:	Not less than 99.80 per cent by wt.
Moisture	:	Not more than 0.1 per cent by wt.
Sulphur dioxide	:	Not more than 70 p.p.m.

BURA

Bura shall contain not less than 96.5 per cent by total sugars expressed as sucrose and shall not contain more than half per cent of its weight as ash insoluble in dilute hydrochloric acid.

In the case of *khandsari*, the minimum sugar content in terms of sucrose shall not be less than 90 per cent.

Bura and *khandsari* may contain sulphur dioxide in concentration not exceeding 70 parts per million.

HONEY

Means the food derived entirely from the work of bees operating upon the nectar of flowers and other sweet exudation of plants. It shall not contain more than (a) 25% of moisture, (b) 0.5 per cent ash and (c) 5 per cent of sucrose except in the case of *Carbia callosa* and Honey dew where the maximum sucrose content shall be 10 per cent. The Minimum reducing sugar content (expressed as invert sugar) shall be 65% except in the case of *Carbiua callosa* and Honey dew where it shall be 60 per cent. Fructose/Glucose ratio shall not be less than 0.90. Fieshe's test should ordinarily be negative.

ICE-CANDY OR ICE LOLLIES OR EDIBLE ICES

Ice-candy or Ice Lollies or Edible Ices "by whatever name it is sold, means the frozen ice produce which may contain the permitted flavours and colours, sugar, syrup, fruit, fruit juices, nuts, cocoa, citric acid, stabilizers or emulsifiers not exceeding 0.5 per cent. It shall not contain any artificial sweetened.

GUR OR JAGGERY

Gur or Jaggery means the product obtained by processing juice pressed out of sugarcane or extracted from palmyra palm, date palm or coconut palm. It shall be free from substances deleterious to health and shall conform to the following analytical standards on dry weight basis:

(1) Total sugars expressed as invert sugar not less than 90 per cent and sucrose not less than 69 per cent.

(2) Extraneous matter insoluble in water not more than 2 per cent.

(3) Total ash not more than 6 per cent

(4) Ash insoluble in hydrochloric acid (HCl) not more than 0.5 per cent.

Gur or jaggery other than that of the liquid or semi-liquid variety shall not contain more than 10 per cent moisture.

Gur or jaggery may contain sulphur dioxide in concentration not exceeding 70 parts per million.

Gur or jaggery means the product obtained by boiling or processing juice pressed out of sugarcane or extracted from palmyra palm, date palm or coconut palm. It is not disputed that "*Shakkar*" is a product obtained by boiling a processing juice from out of sugarcane and therefore it si clear that *shakkar* is jaggery.

CUBE SUGAR

Means the sugar in the from of cube or cuboid blocks manufactured from refined crystallized sugar. It shall be white in colour, free from dirt and other extraneous contamination. It shall conform to the following standards:

Sucrose	:	Not less than 99.7 per cent by weight.
Moisture	:	Not more than 0.25 per cent by weight.
Total ash	:	Not more than 0.03 per cent by weight.
Sulphur dioxide	:	Not more than 70 p.p.m.

DEXTROSE

Is a white or light cream granular powder, odourless and having a sweet taste.

When heated with potassium solution it shall produce a copious precipitate of cuprous oxide. It shall conform to the following standards:

Sulphated ash	:	Not more than 0.1 per cent on dry basis.
Acidity	:	5.0 g dissolved in 50 ml. of freshly boiled and cooled water requires for neutralization not more than 0.20 ml. of N/10 sodium hydroxide to phenolphthalein indicator.
Glucose	:	Not less than 99.0 per cent on dry basis.
Sulphur dioxide	:	Content shall not exceed 70 p.p.m.

GOLDEN SYRUP

Means the syrup obtained by inversion of sugar. It shall be golden yellow in colour, pleasant in taste and free from crystallization. It shall conform to the following standards:

Moisture	:	Not more than 25.0 per cent by weight.
Total ash	:	Not more than 2.5 per cent by weight.
Total sugar as invert sugar	:	Not less than 72.0 per cent by weight.
Sulphur dioxide	:	Content shall not exceed 70.0 p.p.m.

ICING SUGAR

Means the sugar manufactured by pulverizing refined sugar or vacuum pan (Plantation white) sugar with or without edible starch. Edible starch, if added, shall be uniformly extended in the sugar. It shall be in form of white powder, free from dust, or any other extraneous matter. It shall conform to the following standards:

Total starch (moisture free)	:	Not less than 99.0% by weight and sucrose
Moisture	:	Not more than 0.80% by weight.

Starch · Not more than 5.0% by weight on dry basis.

SACCHARIN SODIUM

Commonly known as soluble *sacckar* in having an empirical formula as $C_7H_4Nh_aO_3S$, $2H_2O$ and molecular weight as 241.2 shall be the material which is soluble at 20°C in 1.5 parts of water and 50 parts of alcohol (95 per cents; and shall contain not less than 98.0 per cent and not more than the equivalent of 140.5 per cent of $C_7H_4O_3$ NsNa calculated with reference to the substance dried to constant weight at 105°C, assay being carried out as presented in Indian Pharmacopoeia. It shall not contain more than 2 p.p.m. of arsenic and 10 p.p.m. of lead. The melting point of Saccharin isolated from the material as per Indian Pharmacopoeia method, shall be between 226°C and 230°C. The loss on drying of the material at 105°C shall not less than 12.0 per cent and not more than 16.0 per cent of its weight.

The material shall satisfy the tests of identification and shall conform to the limit tests for free acid or alkali, ammonium compounds and parasulpha molybenzoate as mentioned in the Indian Pharmacopoeia.

CHAPTER 11

VANASPATI, VINEGAR AND GELETIN

Any refined edible vegetable oil or oils, subjected to a process of hydrogenation in any form. It shall be prepared by hydrogenation from groundnut oil, cotton seed oil and sesame oil or mixtures thereof or any other harmless vegetable oils allowed by the Government for the purpose. It shall conform to the standards specified below:

(1) It shall not contain any harmful colouring, flavouring or any other matter deleterious to health;

(2) No colour shall be added to hydrogenated vegetable oil unless so authorized by Government, but in no event any colour resembling the colour of ghee shall be added;

(3) If any flavour is used, it shall be distinct from that of *ghee*, in accordance with a list of permissible flavours and in such quantities as may be prescribed by Government;

Provided that diacetyl to the extent of not more than 4.0 p.p.m. may be added to Vanaspati exclusively meant for consumption by the Armed Forces:

(4) It shall not have moisture exceeding 0.25 per cent;

(5) The melting point as determined by capillary slip method shall be from 31°C to 37°C both inclusive;

(6) The Bytyro-refractometer reading as 40°C, shall not be less than 48;

(7) It shall not have unsaponsifiable matter exceeding 1.25 per cent;

(8) It shall not have free fatty acids (calculated as Oleic acid) exceeding 0.25 per cent;

(9) The product on melting shall be clear in appearance and shall be free from staleness or rancidity, and pleasant to taste and smell;

(10) It shall contain raw or refined sesame (*til*) oil not less than 5 per cent by weight, but sufficient so that when the vanaspati is mixed with refined groundnut oil in the proportion of 20:80, the colour produced by the Baudouin test shall not be lighter than 2.0 red units in a 1 cm. cell on a Lovibond scale;

(11) It shall contain not less than 25 I.U. of synthetic Vitamin 'A' per gram;

(12) No anti-oxidant, synergist, emulsifier or any other such substance shall be added to it except with the prior sanction of the Government.

BAKERY SHORTENING

Vanaspati conforming to standards prescribed above except that:

(1) The melting point as determined by the capillary slip method shall not exceed 41°C,

(2) If aerated, only nitrogen air any other inert gas shall be used for the purpose and the quantity of such gas incorporated in the product shall not exceed 12 per cent by volume thereof.

VINEGAR

A liquid derived from alcoholic and acetous fermentation of any suitable medium such as fruits, malt, molasses, sugarcane juice etc.

Vinegar shall conform to the following standards:

(1) It shall contain at least 3.75 grammes of acetic acid per 100 ml.

(2) It shall contain at least 1.5 per cent w/v of total solids and 0.18 per cent of ash.

(3) It shall not contain: (i) sulphuric acid or any other mineral acids, (ii) lead or copper, (iii) arsenic in amounts exceeding 1.5 parts per million, and (iv) any foreign substance of colouring matter except caramel.

(4) Malt vinegar, in addition, shall have at least 0.05 per cent of phosphorus pentoxide (P_2O_5) and 0.04 per cent of nitrogen.

Brewed vinegar shall not be fortified with acetic acid.

SYNTHETIC VINEGAR

The product prepared from acetic acid. It shall contain not less than 3.75 grams of acetic acid per 100 ml.

It shall not contain –

(1) Sulphuric or any other mineral acid,

(2) Lead or copper,

(3) Arsenic in amounts exceeding 1.5 parts per million,

(4) Any colouring matter, except caramel.

Synthetic vinegar shall be distinctly labeled as Synthetic Prepared from Acetic Acid.

CATECHU (EDIBLE)

Catechu (Edible) shall be the dried aqueous extract prepared from the heart-wood of Acacia catechu. It shall be free from infestation, sand, earth or other dirt and shall conform to the following standards:

(1) 5 ml. of 1 per cent aqueous solution, 0.1 per cent solution of ferric ammonium sulphate shall give a dark green colour, which on the addition of sodium hydroxide solution shall change to purple.

(2) When dried to constant weight at 100°C, it shall not lose more than 12 per cent of its weight.

(3) Water insoluble residue (dried at 100°C) shall not be more than 25 per cent by weight.

(4) Alcohol insoluble residue in 90 per cent alcohol dried at 100°C – not more than 30 per cent by weight.

(5) Total ash on dry basis – not more than 8 per cent alcohol dried at 100°C – not more than 30 per cent by weight.

(6) Ash insoluble in HCl – not more than 0.5 per cent on dry weight basis.

GELATIN

Shall be purified product obtained by partial hydrolysis of collagen, derived from the skin white connective tissues and bones of animals. It shall be colourless or pale yellowish and translucent in the form of sheets, flakes, shreds or coarse to fine powder. It shall have very slight odour and taste but not objectionable which is characteristic and bouillon like. It is stable in air when dry but is subject to microbial decomposition when moist or in solution. It shall not contain:

(1) More than 1.5 per cent moisture;

(2) More than 3.0 per cent of total ash

(3) More than 1000 parts per million of sulphur dioxide;

(4) Less than 15 per cent of nitrogen on dry weight basis.

Gelatin meant for human consumption should be labeled as "Gelatin-Food Grade"

CHAPTER 12

SWEETS AND CONFECTIONERY

HARD BOILED SUGAR CONFECTIONERY

Hard boiled sugar confectionery shall mean a confectionery product which is a supercooled solution of combination of sucrose and liquid glucose (or cane sugar alone) treated with a doctoring agent, such as cream of tartar (*potassium acid tartrate*) with or without the addition of one of more of the following:

(1) Permitted flavouring agents;

(2) Permitted colours;

(3) Acidulant;

(4) Filling;

(5) Any other wholesome ingredient such as fruit or fruit products or edible fat or milk products or cocoa products or nut product or other wholesome ingredients.

It shall conform to the following specification;

Ash, sulphated, per cent by weight	:	Not more than 1.5.
Ash insoluble in dilute HCl	:	Not more than 0.2% by weight

It may contain sulphur dioxide in concentration exceeding 350 parts per million.

TOFFEES

Plain Toffee

It shall be made out of sugar, vanaspati, milk fat or any edible oil and in addition, any of the following material may also be used in its manufacture:

Edible common salt;	Edible groundnut flour;
Starches, edible;	Gelatine, edible;
Gur;	Honey;
Liquid glucose;	Malt Syrup;
Vitamins	Citric acid;
Cream of tartar;	Permitted flavouring agents;
Permitted colours;	Sorbitol;
Tartaric Acid;	Permitted antioxidants and emulsifiers.

Milk Toffee

It shall be made out of sugar, vanaspati, milk fat or any edible oil and milk in any form and in addition may contain any of the materials used of plain toffee.

Modified Toffee

It shall be made of the ingredients used for plain toffee or milk toffee. In addition, it may contain one or more of the following:

Chocolate;	
Cocoa;	
Coffee;	Dried fruits; and
	Nuts

Butter Toffee

It shall be made out of ingredients used for plain toffee, milk toffee or modified toffee; but it shall contain not less than 5 per cent butter by weight.

Toffees shall also comply with the requirements given in Table 12.1

Table 12.1 Requirements for Toffees

Sl. No.	Characteristics	Plain Toffee	Milk Toffee	Modified Toffee	Butter Toffee
(1)	(2)	(3)	(4)	(5)	(6)
1.	Ash, sulphated per cent by weight not more than	2.5	2.5	2.5	2.5
2.	Ash insoluble in dilute hydrochloric acid per cent by weight not more than	0.2	0.2	0.2	0.2
3.	Reducing sugar (calculated as dextrose) per cent by weight not less than	10.0	10.0	10.0	10.0
4.	Sucrose per cent by weight not more than	60.0	60.0	60.0	60.0
5.	Fat, per cent weight (on dry basis) not less than	4.0	4.0	4.0	4.0
6.	Total protein (N_X 6.25) per cent weight, not less than	—	3.0	—	—

LOZENGES

Lozenges shall be made of the following materials, namely:

(1) Pulverized sugar, obtained by powdering vacuum pan sugar or refined sugar, or icing sugar;

(2) Binding materials, such as edible gelatine, edible gums, liquid glucose, dextrins;

(3) Permitted colours;

(4) Permitted flavouring agents.

In addition to the above ingredients, the following ingredients may also be added to the mixture, namely:

Ginger, cinnamon, aniseed, caraway, cardamom, and other spices in powder form or extracts, vitamins, edible common salt, citric acid and sodium bicarbonate, lubricants such as stearic talc (not exceeding 0.1 per cent).

It shall also comply with the following requirements, namely:

(1)	Sulphated ash, per cent by weight	: Not more than 3.0
(2)	Ash insoluble in dilute hydrochloric acid per cent by weight	: Not more than 0.1
(3)	Sucrose, per cent by weight	: Not less than 85.0

CHAPTER 13

FOOD COLOURS

TARTRAZINE

Common Name	:	Tartrazine.
Synonyms	:	Hydrazine Yellow, Tartar Yellow, Acid Yellow, FD & C Yellow No. 5, C. I. Food Yellow 4, Lebensmittel Yellow No. 2.
Colour	:	Colour of the 0.1 per cent [w/v] solution in distilled water—Yellow.
Colour Index No.	:	[1956]—No. 19140
	:	[1924]—No. 640
Class	:	Pyrazolone.
Chemical Name	:	Trisodium salt at 4-(4'-Sulpho-1'-phenylazo)-1-(4'-Sulphoneyl)-5-Hydroxy-pyrazol-3-Carboxylic acid.
Empirical Formula	:	$C_{16}H_9N_4O_9S_2Na_3$
Molecular weight	:	534.4

The material shall not contain more than 10 parts per million of copper and 20 parts per million of chromium when tested by the method prescribed in 3 and 4 of IS: 1969 (part II) – 1963 Methods of Sampling and Test for Coaltar Food Colours, Part II.

Tartrazine shall also comply with the requirements given in Table 13.1.

Table 13.1 Requirements of Tartrazine

Sl. No.	Characteristic	Requirements
(1)	(2)	(3)
1	Pure dye content, per cent by weight, not less than	85
2.	Volatile matter at 135°C per cent by weight, not more than	10
3.	Water-insoluble matter, by weight not more than	0.5
4.	Combined either extract, per cent by weight, not more than	0.3
5.	Subsidiary dyes, per cent by weight, not more than	3.0
6.	Phenylhydrazine-p-sulphonic acid, per cent by weight, not more than	0.5
7.	Mixed oxides, per cent by weight, not more than	1.0
8.	Arsenic, parts per million, not more than	1.0
9	Lead, parts per million, not more than	10.0

The material shall not contain more than 10 parts per million of copper and 20 parts per million of chromium when tested by the methods prescribed in 3 and 4 of IS: 1969 (Part II) – 1963 Methods of Sampling and Test for Coaltar Food Colours, Part II

Sunset Yellow FCF shall also comply with the requirements, given in Table 13.2.

AMARANTH

Common Name : *Amaranth*

Synonyms : Bordeaux S, FD & C Red No. 2, Naphthol Red S, Acid Crimson Azorubine. Brilliant Bordeaux B, Bordeaux Acide B, Amaranthe, C. I. Food Red 9.

Colour : Colour of the 0.1 per cent (w/v) solution in distilled water-Red.

Colour Index No. : (1956)-No. 16185
(1924)-No. 184

Class : Monoazo.

Chemical Name : Trisodium salt of 1-(4'-Sulpho, 1'-naphthylazo) 2-hydroxynaphthlene-3: 6-disulphonic acid.

Empirical Formula : $C_{20}H_{11}N_2OS_2Na_2$

Molecular Weight : 604.5

Table 13.2: Requirement of Sunset Yellow

Sl. No.	Characteristic	Requirements
1.	Pure dye content, per cent by weight, not less than	85
2.	Volatile matter at 135°C per cent by weight, not more than	10
3.	Water-insoluble matter, by weight not more than	0.5
4.	Combined either extract, per cent by weight, not more than	0.3
5.	Subsidiary dyes, per cent by weight, not more than	3.0
6.	Phenylhydrazine-p-sulphonic acid, per cent by weight, not more than	0.5
7.	Mixed oxides, per cent by weight, not more than	1.0
8.	Arsenic, parts per million, not more than	1.0
9.	Lead, parts per million, not more than	10.0

The material shall not contain more than 10 parts per million of copper and 20 parts per million of chromium when tested by the methods prescribed in 3 and 4 of the IS: 1699 (Part II) – 1963 methods of Sampling and Test for coaltar food colours, Part II.

Amaranth shall also comply with the requirements, given in Table 13.3:

Table 13.3: Requirements of *Amaranth*

Sl. No.	Characteristic	Requirements
1	Pure dye content, per cent by weight, not less than	85
2.	Volatile matter at 135°C per cent by weight, not more than	10
3.	Water-insoluble matter, by weight not more than	0.5
4.	Combined either extract, per cent by weight, not more than	0.2
5	Subsidiary dyes (as fast red E) per cent by weight, not more than	4.0
6.	Mixed oxides, per cent by weight, not more than	1.0
7.	Arsenic, parts per million, not more than	1.0
8.	Lead, parts per million, not more than	10.6

ERYTHROSINE

Common Name : Erythrosine

Synonyms : Soluble Primrose, Pyrosine B, FD & C Red No.3, Iodosine B, Erythrosine BS, Erythrosine J, Erythrosine Extra Bluish, C.I., Food Red 14.

Colour : Colour of the 0.1 per cent (w/v) solution in distilled water-Red

Colour Index No. : (1956) – No. 45430
: (1924) – No. 773

Class : Xanthene

Chemical Name : Disodium or potassium salt of tetra-iodofluorescein or of hydroxytetra-iodo-o-carboxy-phenyl fluorene

Empirical Formula : $C_{20}H_6O_5I_4Na_2$

Molecular Weight : 879.9 (disodium salt).

The material shall not contain more than 10 parts per million of copper and 20 parts per million of chromium when tested by the methods prescribed in 3 and 4 of IS: 1699 (Part II) – 1963 Methods of sampling and test for coaltar food colours, Part II.

Erythrosine shall also comply with the requirements, given in the Table 13.4:

Table 13.4: Requirements of Erythrosine

Sl. No.	Characteristic	Requirements
1	Pure dye content, per cent by weight, not less than	85
2	Volatile matter at 135°C per cent by weight, not more than	10
3.	Water-insoluble matter, by weight not more than	0.5
4	Combined either extract, per cent by weight, not more than	0.2
5	Subsidiary dyes per cent by weight, not more than	4.0
6	Mixed oxides, per cent by weight, not more than	1.0
7.	Organically bound iodine in the anhydrous pure dye, (per cent by weight)	55.8 to 58.5
8.	Arsenic, parts per million, not more than	1.0
9	Lead, parts per million, not more than	10.6

INDIGO CARMINE

Common name : Indigo Carmine

Synonyms : Indigotin, Indigo Extract, Saxony, Blue, FD & C Blue No. 2, C. Food Blue 1, Lebensmittel,
Blue No. 2.

Colour : Colour of the 0.1 per cent (w/v) solution in distilled

Water : Blue

Colour Index No. : (1956) – No. 73015
(1924) – No. 1180

Class : Indigoid

Chemical Name : Disodium salt of indigotin – 5:5'-Disuphonic acid.

Empirical Formula : $C_{16}H_8N_2O_8S_2Na_2$

Molecular Weight : 466.4

The material shall not contain more than 10 parts per million of copper and 20 parts per million of chromium, when tested by the methods prescribed in 3 and 4 of the IS: 1699 (Part II) – 1963 methods of sampling and test for Coal Tar Food Colours, Part II.

Indigo carmine shall also comply with the requirements, given in the Table 13.5:

Table 13.5: Requirements of Indigo Carmine

Sl. No.	Characteristic	Requirements
1	Pure dye content, per cent by weight, not less than	85
2	Volatile matter at 135°C per cent by weight, not more than	10
3	Water-insoluble matter, by weight not more than	0.5
4	Combined either extract, per cent by weight, not more than	0.2
5	Lower sulphonated dyes (sodium indigomonosulphobonate) per cent by weight, not more than	5.0
6	Mixed oxides, per cent by weight, not more than	1.0
7	Arsenic, parts per million, not more than	1.0
8	Lead, parts per million, not more than	10.6

β-CAROTENE

β-Carotene is obtained as dark violet hexagonal prisms when crystallized from benzene-methanol solution; or as red rhombic almost quadratic plates, from petroleum ether.

Synonyms	:	C.I. natural yellow 26.
Colour Index No.	:	No. 75130 (1956)
Class	:	Carotenoids
Chemical Name	:	All trans β-Carotene.
Empirical Formula	:	$C_{40}H_{56}$
Molecular Weight	:	536.89
Melting Point	:	183° ± 1°C.

Solubility

Soluble in carbon disulfide, benzene and chloroform, moderately soluble in normal hexane, cyclohexane ether, petroleum ether and oils; practically insoluble in methanol and ethanol; insoluble in water;

Spectrophotometric Requirement

The wavelengths absorption maxima of all trans b-Carotene in cyclohexane (0.2 mg per 100 ml. approximately) and in 1 cm, cell shall be 456 mμ to 484 mμ region. There shall be no *cis*-peak in the 330 mμ to 355 mμ region.

A solution of β-Carotene in chloroform on addition of antimony trichloride solution shall give a dark blue colour having maximum absorption at a wavelength of 590 mμ.

Colour Reaction

When 2 ml of concentrated sulphuric acid is added to 2 ml. of 0.2 per cent solution of β-Carotene in chloroform, the acid layer shall turn blue.

The material shall have a minimum purity of 96.0 per cent.

Maximum limit of metallic impurities shall be:

Arsenic (as As)	:	5 p.p.m.
Lead (as Pb)	:	20 p.p.m.

CHLOROPHYLL

The green pigment of plants, is extracts and widely used as a colouring matter for various food items:

Synonyms	:	C.I. Natural green 3; Lebensmittel – Green No. 1
Colour	:	Green
Colour Index No.	:	(1956) No. 75810 (1924) No. 12499
Class	:	Phorbin (dihydrophorbin)
Chemical Name	:	Chlorophyll a-magnesium complex of 1,3,5, 8-tetramethyl 4-ethyl-2-vinyl-keto-10-carbo-methoxyphorbiphytyl-7-propiionate. Chlorophyll b-magnesium complex of 1, 5, 8-trimethyl 3-formyl-4-ethyl-2-vinyl-9-keto-10-carbo-methoxyphorbinphytyl-7-propionate.
Empirical Formula	:	Chlorophyll a-$C_{55}H_{72}O_5N_4Mg$.
	:	Chlorophyll b-$C_{55}H_{72}O_5N_4Mg$.
Molecular Weight	:	Chlorophyll a-893.54
	:	Chlorophyll b-907.52

General—The material shall be intensely dark green aqueous ethanolic, or oily solution of chlorophyll degradation products. It shall be soluble in ethanol, chloroform and benzene.

Identification tests – A solution of chlorophyll in ethanol shall be blue with deep red fluorescence.

Brown-phase Reaction. – When green ether or petroleum ether solution of chlorophyll is treated with a small quantity of a 10 per cent solution of potassium hydroxide in methanol the colour shall become brown quickly returning to green.

Note: - This test is applicable only when chlorophyll has not been treated with alkalis.

Maximum limits for metallic impurities shall be:

Arsenic (As)	:	5 ppm
Lead (Pb)	:	20 ppm.
Copper (Cu)	:	30 ppm
Zine (Zn)	:	50 ppm

CARAMEL

Caramel shall be prepared from the food grade carbohydrates or their combinations given below by the action of heat, in the presence or absence of acids or alkalis or salts. The material be water soluble. It shall also be free from extraneous colouring matter.

Raw Material

1. *Carbohydrates*: Caramel shall be prepared from the following food grad carbohydrates or their mixtures:

   (a) Dextrose

   (b) Invert sugar

   (c) Lactose

   (d) Malt syrup

   (e) Sucrose, and

   (f) Glucose syrup

(2) *Acids:* The following acids alkalies may be employed to assist caramelization:

(a) Acids

   (i) Acetic acid,

   (ii) Citric acid,

(iii) Phosphoric acid,

(iv) Sulphuric Acid

(v) Sulphur dioxide, and

(vi) Carbonic acid.

(b) Alkalies

(i) Ammonia or ammonium hydroxide,

(ii) Potassiumhydroxide, and

(iii) Sodium hydroxide

(3) *Salts* – Ammonium, sodium or potassium carbonate (including bicarbonate), phosphate (including dibasic phosphate and monobasic phosphate). Sulphate and Sulphite may be used.

Emulsifying and stabilizing agents as permitted in this rule may be added.

Identification

(a) When 0.5 ml. of phosphoric is added to 20 ml. of 5 per cent w/v solution of caramel, na precipitate shall be formed.

(b) When one part of caramel is dissolved in 100 parts of water, it shall yield a clear solution having a distinct colour. On exposure to sunlight for 6 hours the colours of this solution shall not change and no precipitate shall be formed.

The minimum density (g/m) of 10 per cent solution of the material shall be 1.023.

Maximum limits for metallic impurities shall be:

Copper (as Cu)	: 30 p.p.m.
Arsenic (as As)	: 5 p.p.m.
Lead (as Pb)	: 5 p.p.m.

ANNATTO

The material shall be of the following two types:

(a) Solution in oil for use in butter and other food products, and

(b) Solution in water for use in cheese and other food products.

The material shall be derived only from the plant *Bixa orecallana* L. and shall not contain any extraneous colouring matter. It shall be manufactured and packed under hygienic conditions.

(i) Solution of Annatto colour in oil for use in butter and other food products.

Only the vegetable oils included in these rules shall be used either singly or in combination.

The solution of Annatto colour in oil shall be clear and shall remain so on storage in suitable containers at 15°C except for slight deposit of stearin.

Colour – The colour of the solution in amylacetate at a dilution of 1:1000 (w/v) when measured in a Lovibond Tintometer with a 1 cm cell shall be not less than the following.

Yellow units	:	5.0
Red units	:	0.4

or be equivalent to the colour of the following inorganic solution at a liquid depth of one centimeter which may be employed for matching the stated dilution in plunger type calorimeter using incident light closely approximating the north day light:

Potassium	:	0.320 g
Cobalt Ammonium Sulphate $[C_0SO_4(NH_2)_2SO_4 6H_2O]$	:	2.02 g
Sulphuric acid, sp. Gr. (1.84)	:	2 ml.

Distilled Water to make solution to 1 litre.

The reagents shall be of the analytical reagent grade.

Although the solution retains its tinctorial value for a considerable time, after prolonged storage, its optical clarity shall be examined before use, to ensure that no alteration has taken place.

(ii) Solution of Annatto colour in water for use in cheese and other food products:

In the preparation of the solution, potable water shall be used, a little quantity (0.5 to 3 per cent) of alkali may be added.

The solution shall be clear and shall remain so on storage in suitable containers at a temperature os 15°C;

Colour – The colour of the solution in 0.1 N sodium hydroxide or potassium hydroxide at a dilution of 1:10,000 (w/v) measured in 1 cm cell shall be the same as that specified in (i) above.

Maximum limit of metallic impurities shall be:

Arsenic (as As)	:	5 p.p.m. max.
Lead (as Pb)	:	20 p.p.m. max.
Copper (as Cu)	:	30 p.p.m. max.

RIBOFLAVIN

Riboflavin is a yellow to orange-yellow crystalline powder, Melting point about 280°C with decomposition.

Solubility-Slightly soluble in water, more soluble in saline solution and in a 10 per cent (w/v) solution of urea, sparingly soluble in alcohol, practically insoluble in chloroform and in solvent ether, and soluble in dilute solution of alkali hydroxides.

Synonyms	:	Vitamin B2, lactoflavin and Lactroflavine.
Colour	:	Yellow to orange-yellow
Class	:	Isoalloxazine.
Chemical Name	:	6: 7-dimethyl-9-(d-l-ribityl)-isoalloxazine.

Empirical Formula : $C_{17}H_{20}N_4O_6$

Molecular Weight : 376.38

Identification

A solution of 1 mg of Riboflavin in 100 ml. water is pale greenish yellow in transmitted light, and has an intense yellowish green fluorescence which disappears on the addition of sodium dithlonite and mineral acide or alkalis.

Spectrophotometry

Absorption maxima of aqueous solution shall be at 220 to 225, 266, 371 and 444 mm.

Specific Rotation

It shall be determined in a 0.5 per cent w/v solution in a mixture of 1.5 ml of 0.1 N alcoholic solution of potassium hydroxide (free from carbonate) and sufficient freshly boiled and cooled water to produce 10 ml. The specific rotation, when calculated with reference to the substance dried to constant weight in the dark of 105°C, shall be – 122°.

The material shall have minimum purity of 97.0 per cent.

Maximum limit of metallic impurities shall be:

Arsenic (as As) : 5 p.p.m.

Lead (as Pb) : 20 p.p.m.

PONCEAU 4R

Common Name : Ponceau 4R

Synonyms : C.I. Food Red 7, labensmittel Rot No. 4, Coccine Nouvelle, Cochineal A; E.E.C. Serial No. E.124

Colour of the 0.1% per cent (m/v) solution in distilled water : Red

Colour Index No. : (1956) No. 16255

Class : Monoazo

Chemical Name : Trisodium salt of 1-(4-Sulpho-1-1naphthylazo)-2-naphthol-6, 8-disulphonic acid.

Empirical Formula : $C_{20}H_{11}N_2O_{10}S_3Na_3$

Molecular Weight : 604.5

General requirements: The material shall be free from mercury, selenium and chromium in any form, aromatic nitro compounds, aromatic hydrocarbons and cyanides.

Ponceau 4R shall also comply with the requirements, given in Table 13.6:

Table 13.6: Requirements of Ponceau

Sl. No.	Characteristic	Requirements
1.	Total dye content per cent by mass corrected for sample dried at 105 ± 1°C for 2 hours	Not less than 80
2.	Volatile matter at 135°C per cent by weight,	Not more than 10
3.	Water-insoluble matter, by weight not more than	Not more than 0.5
4.	Combined either extract, per cent by mass	Not more than 0.5
5.	Subsidiary dyes, per cent by mass	Not more than 1.0
6.	Dye intermediate, per cent by mass	Not more than 0.5
7.	Arsenic, parts per million	Not more than 3
8.	Lead, parts per million	Not more than 10

CARMOISINE

Common Name : Carmoisine

Synonyms : Azorubine, C.I. Food Red 3, E.E.C. Serial No. E122.

Colour of the 0.1% (m/v) solution in Distilled water : Red

Colour Index No. : (1956) – No. 14720

Class : Monoazo

Chemical Name : Disodium salt of 2-(4-sulpho-1-naphthylazo)-1-naphthol-4-sulphonic acid.

Empirical Formula : $C_{20}H_{12}N_2O_7S_2Na_2$

Molecular Weight : 502.44

The material shall be free from mercury, selenium and chromium in any form, aromatic amines; aromatic-nitro compounds, aromatic, hydrocarbons any cyanides.

Carmoisine shall also comply with the requirements as given in Table 13.7:

Table 13.7: Requirements for Carmoisine

Sl. No.	Characteristic	Requirements
1.	Total dye content per cent by mass corrected for sample dried at 105 ± 1°C for 2 hours	Not less than 80
2.	Volatile matter at 135°C per cent by weight, not more than	Not more than 10
3.	Water-insoluble matter, by weight not more than	Not more than 0.5
4.	Combined either extract, per cent by mass	Not more than 0.5
5.	Subsidiary dyes, per cent by mass	Not more than 1.0
6.	Dye intermediate, per cent by mass	Not more than 0.5
7.	Arsenic, parts per million	Not more than 3
8.	Lead, parts per million	Not more than 10

FAST RED E

Common Name	:	Fast Red E
Synonyms	:	C. I. Food Red 4, Roung Solide E
Colour of the 0.1% (m/v) solution in Distilled water	:	Red
Colour Index No.	:	(1956) – No. 16045
Class	:	Monoazo
Chemical Name	:	Disodium salt of 1-(4-Sulpho-1-naphthylazo)-2-napthhol-6-Sulphonic acid
Empirical Formula	:	$C_{20}H_{12}N_2O_7S_2Na_2$
Molecular Weight	:	502.44

The materials shall be free from mercury, selenium and chromium in any from, aromatic amines, aromatic nitro compounds, aromatic hydrocarbons, and cyanides.

Fast Red E shall also comply with the requirements, given in Table 13.8:

Table 13.8: Requirements of Fast Red E

Sl. No.	Characteristic	Requirements
1	Total dye content per cent by mass corrected for sample dried at 105 ± 1°C for 2 hours	Not less than 80
2.	Volatile matter at 135°C per cent by mass	Not more than 10
3.	Water-insoluble matter, per cent by mass	Not more than 0.5
4.	Combined either extract, per cent by mass	Not more than 0.5
5.	Subsidiary dyes, per cent by mass	Not more than 1.0
6.	Dye intermediate, per cent by mass	Not more than 0.5
7.	Arsenic, parts per million	Not more than 3
8.	Lead, parts per million	Not more than 10

COAL TAR FOOD COLOUR PREPARATIONS AND MIXTURES

Colour preparation: Colour preparation means a preparation containing one or more of the permitted coal for food colours along with diluents and/or filler material and meant to be used for imparting colours to foods.

Colour mixture: Colour mixture means a mixture of two or more permitted coal tar food colours without diluents and filler material and meant to be used for imparting colours to foods.

Permitted coal tar food colours used in preparation or in mixture shall conform to relevant prescribed specifications. The colour preparation shall be either in the form of liquid or powder. The liquid preparation shall be reasonably free from sediments. The powder preparation shall be reasonably free from lumps and any visible extraneous or foreign matter, Colour preparation or mixture may contain preservatives and stabilizers permitted under these rules.

Only the following diluents or filler materials shall be permitted to be used in colour preparation, namely:

(a) Potable water
(b) Edible common salt
(c) Sugar
(d) Dextrose moknohydrate
(e) Liquid Glucose
(f) Sodium sulphate
(g) Tartaric acid
(h) Glycerine
(i) Prophylene glycol, food grade
(j) Acetic acid, dilute

(k) Sorbitol, food grade

(l) Citric acid

The total coal tar dye content per cent by mass (m/m) in colour preparation or in mixture shall be declared on the label of the container. In powder preparation, the declared value shall be on moisture free basis and in case of liquid preparation on 'as is basis' and the total dye content shall be within ± 15 per cent of the declared value. Colour preparation and colour mixture shall also comply with the requirements, given in Table 13.9:

Table 13.9: Requirement for Coal Tar Food Colour

Sl. No.	Characteristic	Requirements
1.	Water insoluble matter, per cent by mass	Not more than 1.0
2.	Arsenic, parts per million	Not more than 3
3.	Lead, parts per million	Not more than 10

Note: All requirements shall be on dry basis.

SILVER LEAP (*CHANDI KA WARQ*)

Silver Leap (*Chandi ka Warq*) - food grade - shall be in the form of sheets, free from creases and folds and shall contain not less than 99.9 per cent of silver.

GROUNDNUT KERNEL

Groundnut Kernel (deshelled) for direct human consumption commonly known as *moongphali* are obtained from the plant Arachis hypogols. The kernels shall be free from non-edible seeds such as mahua, castor, neem or argemone etc. It shall be free from colouring matter and preservatives. It shall be practically free from extraneous matter, such as stones, dirt, clay, etc. The kernels shall conform to the following standards, namely:

Moisture	: Not more than 7.0 per cent
Damaged kernel including slightly damaged kernel	: Not more than 5.0 per cent by weight
Aflatoxin content	: Not more than 30 parts per billion.

Without prejudice to the standards laid down in this book, whenever water is used in the manufacture or preparation of any article of food, such water shall be free from micro-organism likely to cause disease and also free from chemical constituents which may impair health.

CHAPTER 14

COLOURING MATTER, PACKAGING AND LABELLING

COLOURING OF FOOD AND BEVERAGES

The addition of a colouring matter to any article of food except as specifically permitted by these rules is prohibited.

Addition of Colouring Matter

Where an extraneous colouring matter has been added to any article of food there shall be written on the label attached to any package of food so coloured a statement in capital letters as below:

Artificially Coloured

Provided that this rule shall not apply to cheese (all classes), ice-cream, mixed, ice-cream, ice-candy, icing-sugar and gelatine desserts.

Use of caramel

Notwithstanding provisions of Rule 24 and Rule 32(c) caramel may be used without label declaration.

Natural colouring matters

Except as otherwise provided in the rules the following natural colouring principles whether isolated from natural colours or produced synthetically may be used in or upon any article of food:

(1) (i) Beta-carotene,

(ii) Beta-apo-8 carotenal,

(iii) Methylester of Beta-apo-8 carotnoic acid,

(iv) Ethylester of Beta-apo-8 carotenoic acid,

(v) Canthaxanthin;

(2) Chlorophyll;

(3) Riboflavin (Lactoflavin);

(4) Caramel;

(5) Annatto;

(6) *Ratanjot*;

(7) Saffron;

(8) Curcumin or turmeric

In the preparation of the solution of annatto colour in oil, castor oil conforming to Indian Pharmacopoeia may be used either singly or in combination with any edible vegetable oil.

ADDITION OF INORGANIC MATTER AND PIGMENTS

Inorganic colouring matters and pigments shall not be added to any article of food.

[The chewing gum may contain Titanium dioxide-(food grade) up to a maximum limit of a 1 per cent]

COAL-TAR DYES

No coal-tar dyes or a mixture thereof except the these given Table 14.1 shall be used in food.

Permitted Coal-tar Dyes

Use of permitted coal-tar dyes in or upon any food other than those enumerated below is prohibited:

Table 14.1: Usable eating in Foods

Sl. No.	Colour	Common name	Colour Index (1956)	Chemical Class
	(1)	(2)	(3)	(4)
1.	Red	Ponceau 4R	16255	Azo
		Carmoisine	14720	"
		Fast Red E	16045	"
		Amaranth	16185	"
		Erythrosine	45430	"
2.	Yellow	Tartrazine	19140	Xanthene
		Sunset Yellow FCF	15985	Pyrazolone
3.	Blue	Indigo Carmine	73015	Indigoid
		Brilliant Blue FCF	42090	Triarylmethane
4.	Green	Green S	44090	Triarylmethane
		Fast Green FCF	42053	Triarylmethane

(1) Ice-cream including mixed ice-cream.

(2) Dairy products except milk, *dahi*, butter, *ghee*, cheese, *chenna*, condensed milk, cream, skimmed milk, butter milk, toned milk, double toned milk, recombined milk, skimmed milk *chenna*, standardized milk *chhenna*, *khoa*, dry whole milk, dry skimmed milk and baby foods.

(3) Biscuit, pastry, confectionery, savouries like *Dalmoth*, *Mongia*, *Phul Gulab*, Papar, sago or plain *Dal Biji*, wafer and similar products and sweets.

(4) Fruit products except as otherwise provided in Appendix B the PFA Act.

(5) Non-alcoholic beverages except tea, cocoa, malted foods and coffee.

(6) Alcoholic beverages (for the period up to and inclusive of the 21st May, 1977).

(7) Custard powder,

(8) Jelly crystals,

(9) Soup powder.

(10) Processed or preserved vegetables.

(11) Flavouring agents.

(12) Ice-candy and

(13) Sweetened ice, thread candies and similar products.

Maximum Limit of Permitted Colours

The maximum limit of any permitted coal-tar colours or mixture of permitted coal-tar colours which may be added to any food enumerated in Rule 29 shall not exceed 0.2 gram per kilogram of the final food or beverage for consumption.

Colours to be Pure

The colours specified in Rule 28 when used in the preparation of any article of food shall be pure and free from any harmful impurities.

PACKAGING AND LABELLING OF FOODS

Contents of the Label

Unless otherwise provided in these rules there shall be specified on every label:

(1) The name, trade name or description of food contained in the package.

(2) The name and business address of the manufacturer or importer or vendor or packer.

(3) Where any permitted Class II preservative and/or permitted colouring agent and/or permitted antioxidant and/or vitamin anti-caking agent and/or stabilizing agent and/or emulsifying agent and/or mineral is added, a statement to the effect that it contains permitted Class II preservatives and/or permitted colouring agents and/or

permitted antioxidants and/or vitamins, anticaking agent and/or stabilizing agent and/or emulsifying agent and/or mineral.

(4) The net weight or number or measure or volume of contents as the circumstances may require except in the case of biscuits, bread, confectionery and sweets where the weight may be expressed in terms of either average net weight and/or minimum net weight.

(5) A batch number or code number either in Hindi or English numericals or alphabets or in combination:

In the case of food package weighing not more than 60 grams particulars under class (d) or (e) need not be specified:

Provided further that in the case of:

(1) Carbonated water container, and

(2) A package containing more than 60 grams but not more than 120 grams of biscuits, confectionery and sweets; particulars under clauses (d) and (e) need not be specified:

In the case of a package containing bread, and milk in bottles, including sterilized milk, particulars under clause (e) need not be specified.

The term 'label' means a display of written, printed, perforated, stenciled, embossed or stamped matter upon the container cover, lid and/or crown cork of any food package.

A batch number or code number is a mark of identification by which the food can be traced in manufacture and identified in distribution.

NUTRITIONAL FOOD

The food claimed to be enriched with nutrients such as minerals, proteins or vitamins shall give the quantities of such added nutrients on the label.

Languages of the Particulars or Declaration of the Label

The particulars of declaration required under these rules to be specified on the label shall be in English or Hindi in Devnagari script:

Provided that nothing herein contained shall prevent the use of any other language in addition to the language required under this rule.

Declaration to be Surrounded by Line

There shall be a surrounding line enclosing the declaration and where the words "unsuitable for babies" are required to be used there shall be another such line enclosing these words.

Distance of Surrounding Line

The distance between any apart of the words "unsuitable for babies" and the surrounding line enclosing these words shall not be less than 1.5 mm

Size of Types Used for Declaration

The types used for declaration shall be of such dimension that it shall be conspicuous to a reader and shall not be in any case less than 3 mm in height. The word 'Synthetic' whenever it is used shall be of the same size as used for the name of the product.

Labels not to Contain False or Misleading Statements

A label shall not contain any statement, claim, design, device, fancy name or abbreviation which is false or misleading in any particular concerning the food contained in the package, or concerning the quantity or the nutritive value or in relation to the place of origin of the said food:

This rule shall not apply in respect of established trade or fancy names of confectionery, biscuits and sweets such as Barley, Sugar, Bulls Eye, Cream Cracker, or in respect of aerated waters such as Ginger Beer or Gold Spot or any other name in existence in international trade practice.

Labels for Proprietary or Fancy Trade Names

In all types of proprietary foods, where fancy names or trade names are used, the name of the food or category under which it falls in these rules shall also be mentioned on the label. In case it cannot be classified in any of the standards prescribed in Appendix B of the PFA Act then the names of the ingredients used in the products in descending order of composition shall be indicated on the label subject to approval of the Central Committee for Food Standards.

Fancy trade name or proprietary name means the non-conventional type of food which has not been standardized under the Prevention of Food Adulteration Act, 1954.

Labels not to Contain Reference to Act or Rules Contradictory to Required Particulars

The label shall not contain any reference to the Act or any of these rules or any comment on, or reference to, or explanation of any particulars or declaration required by the act or any of these rules to be included in the label which directly or by implication, contradicts, qualifies or modifies such particulars or declaration.

Labels not to use words Implying Recommendations by Medical Profession

There shall not appear in the label of any package containing food for sale the words "recommended by the medical profession" or any words which imply or suggest that the food is recommended, prescribed, or approved by medical practitioners.

Unauthorised use of Words showing Imitation Prohibited

There shall not be written in the statement or label attached to any package containing any article of food the word "imitation" or any word, or words implying that the article is a substitute for any food, unless the use of the said word or words is specifically permitted under these rules.

Any fruit syrup, fruit juice, fruit squash, fruit beverage or cordial or crush which does not contain the prescribed amount of fruit juice, shall not be described as a fruit syrup, fruit syrup, fruit squash, fruit beverage or cordial or crush, as the case may be, and shall be described as a synthetic product. Every synthetic product shall be clearly and conspicuously marked on the label as "SYNTHETIC" and no container containing such product shall have a label, whether attached thereto or printed on the wrapper of such container or otherwise, which may lead the consumer into believing that it is a fruit product. Neither the word "FRUIT" shall be used in describing such a product nor shall it be sold under the cover of a label which carries picture of any fruit. The product containing added natural flavour shall be labeled as "CONTAINS ADDED FLAVOUR" whereas the product containing synthetic flavour, shall be labeled as "ARTIFICIALLY FLAVOLURED"

Carbonated water containing no fruit juice or pulp not have a label which leads the consumer into believing that it is a fruit product.

Any fruit and vegetable product alleged to be fortified with vitamin C shall contain not less than 40 mgm. of a ascorbic acid per 100 g of the product.

Imitations not to be Marked "Pure"

The word "pure" or any word or words of the same significance shall not be included in the label of a package that contains an imitation of any food.

COFFEE-CHICORY MIXTURE: FORM OF LABELS

(i) Every package containing a mixture of coffee and chicory shall have affixed to it a label upon which shall be printed the following declarations.

Coffee blended with Chicory

This mixture contains:

Coffee	:	.....per cent
Chicory	:	.....per cent

CONDENSED MILK OR DESICCATED (DRIED) MILK

Every package containing condensed milk or desiccated (dried) milk shall bear a label upon which is printed such one of the following declaration as may be applicable or such other declaration substantially to the like effect as may be allowed by the State Government.

(1) In the case of condensed milk (unsweetened):

CONDENSED MILK UNSWEETENED (Evaporated Milk) This tin contains the equivalent of (x)..............litres of milk

(2) In the case of condensed milk (sweetened):

CONDENSED MILK SWEETENED This tin contains the equivalent of (x) ....litres of milk with sugar added

(3) In the case of condensed skimmed milk (unsweetened):

CONDENSED SKIMMED MILK UNSWEETENED (Evaporated Skimmed Milk) This tin contains the equivalent of (x).............litres of skimmed milk

(4) In the case of condensed skimmed milk (sweetened):

CONDENSED SKIMMED MILK SWEETENED This tin contains the equivalent of (x).............litres of skimmed milk with sugar added

(5) In the case of condensed milk (sweetened and flvaoured):

This has been flavoured with............NOT TO BE USED FOR INFANTS BELOW SIX MONTHS

(6) In the case of milk powder:

MILK POWDER This tin contains the equivalent of (x)...........litres of milk

(7) In the case of milk powder which contain lecithin:

MILK POWDER IN THIS PACKAGE CONTAINS LECITHIN

(8) In the case of partly skimmed milk powder:

PARTLY SKIMMED MILK POWDER This tin contains the equivalent of (x)............litres of partly skimmed milk having ....per cent milk fat

(9) In the case of skimmed milk powder:

SKIMMED MILK POWDER This tin contains the equivalent of (x)...........litres of skimmed milk

The declaration shall in each case be completed by inserting at (x) the appropriate number in words and in figures, for example, "one and half (1-1/2)" and fraction being expressed as eight quarters or a half, as the case may be. For the purpose of deciding the equivalent of litres of milk or skimmed milk under these rules, 'milk' means milk which contains not less than 12.0 per cent of total milk solids, including not less than 3.5 per cent of milk fat and 'skimmed milk means milk which contains not less than 8.5 per cent of milk solids other than milk fat.

There shall not be placed on any package containing condensed milk or desiccated (dried) milk any comment on, explanation of, or reference to either the statement of equivalence, contained in the prescribed declaration or on the words "machine skimmed', "skimmed" or "unsuitable for babies" except instruction as to dilution as follows:

> "To make a fluid not below the composition of fresh milk or skimmed milk (as the case may be) with the contents of this package add (here insert the number of parts) of water by volume to one part by volume of this condensed milk or desiccated (dried) milk."

Wherever the word "milk" appears on the label of a package of condensed skimmed milk or of desiccated (dried) skimmed milk as the description or part of the description of the contents, it shall be immediately preceded or followed by the word "machine skimmed" or "partly skimmed" as the case may be.

FLUID MILK

The caps of the milk bottles shall clearly indicate the nature of the milk contained in them. The indication may be either in full or by abbreviation shown below:

(1) Buffalo milk may be denoted by the letter : 'B'

(2) Cow milk may be denoted by the letter : 'C'

(3) Goat milk may be denoted by the letter : 'G'

(4) Standardised milk may be denoted by the letter : 'S'

(5) Toned milk may be denoted by the letter : 'T'

(6) Double toned milk may be denoted by the letters : 'DT'

(7) Skimmed milk may be denoted by the letter : 'K'

(8) Pasteurized milk may be denoted by the letter 'P' followed by the class of milk. For example Pasteurized Buffalo milk shall bear the letters : 'PB'.

ICE-CREAM

Every dealer in ice-cream or mixed ice-cream who, in the street or other place of public resort, sells or offers or exposes for sale, ice-cream or ice-candy from a stall or from a cart, barrow or other vehicle, or from a basket, phial, tray or other container used without a staff or a vehicle, shall have his name and address along with the name and address of the manufacturer, if any, legibly and conspicuously displayed on the stall, vehicle or container, as the case may be. Every package of ice-cream, *kulfi*, and chocolate ice-cream containing starch shall have a declaration on a label as specified in sub-rule (2) of Rule 43.

HINGRA

Every container continuing *Hingra* shall bear a label upon which is printed a declaration in the following form, namely:

"This container contains Hingra (Imported) from Iran/ Afghanistan and is certified to be conforming to the standards laid down in the Prevention of Food Adulteration Rules, 1955".

LIGHT BLACK PEPPER

Every package containing light black pepper shall bear the following label in addition to the Agmark seal and the requirement prescribed under Rule 32:

Light Black Pepper (Light berries).

CASSIA BARK

Every package containing "Cassia Bark" shall bear the following label:

CASSIA BARK (TAJ)

CINNAMON

Every package containing "Cinnamon" shall bear the following label:

CINNAMON (*DALCHINI*)

CHILLI

Every package of chillies which contains added edible oil shall bear the following label:

CHILLIES IN THIS PACKAGE CONTAINS AN ADMIXTURE OF NOT MORE THAN 2 PER CENT OF............(NAME OF OIL) EDIBLE OIL

CURRI POWDER

Every package of curry powder shall bear a label upon which is printed a declaration giving percentage of edible common salt and the names of spices in descending order of composition on wt/wt basis.

SKIMMED MILK

Partly skimmed milk powder (sour) used by industry like bakery, containing sodium bicarbonate as a neutralizer shall have a label declaration as "UNIT FOR DIRECT CONSUMPTION".

MASALA

Every package of mixed *masalas* shall bear a label specifying the ingredients of the products in descending order by weight.

COMPOUNDED ASAFOETIDA

Every container of compounded asafetida shall indicate the approximate composition of edible starch or edible cereal flour used in the compound, on the label.

MAIDA

Every package containing *maida* treated with improver or bleaching agents shall carry following label, namely:

WHEAT FLOUR TREATED WITH IMPROVER/ BLEACHING AGENTS, TO BE USED BY BAKERIES ONLY

BLEND A PALMOLEIN GROUNDNUT

Every package containing an admixture of palmolein with groundnut oil shall carry the following label, namely:

BLEND OF PALMOLEIN AND GROUND NUT
Palmolein..............................per cent
Groundnut oil.........................per cent

BLEND OF IMPORTED RAPESEED OIL AND MUSTARD OIL

Every package containing an admixture of imported rapeseed oil with mustard oil, shall carry the following label, namely,

BLEND OF IMPORTED RAPESEED OIL AND MUSTARD OIL
Imported rapeseed oil....................per cent
Mustard oil...................................per cent

COAL-TAAR

Every package of coal-taar food colour preparation and mixture shall bear a label upon which is printed a declaration giving the percentage of totally dye content.

MALTED MILK

Unless otherwise provided in these rules, every package of malted milk food which contains added natural colouring matter except caramel, shall bear the following label:

MALTED MILK FOOD IN THIS PACKAGE CONTAINS PERMITTED NATURAL COLOURING MATTER

MONOSODIUM

Every package of meat product which contains monosodium glutamate, shall bear the following label:

THIS PACKAGE OF...........CONTAINS MONODSODIUM GLUTAMATE, UNFIT FOR INFANTS BELOW 12 MONTHS

NOTES OF ADDITION, ADMIXTURE OR DEFICIENCY IN FOOD

Every advertisement and every price or trade list or label for an article of food which contains an addition, admixture or deficiency shall describe the food as containing such addition, admixture or deficiency and shall also specify the nature and quantity of such addition, admixture or deficiency. No such advertisement or price or trade list or label attached to the container of the food shall contain any words which might imply that the food is pure:

For the purpose of this rule the following shall not be deemed as an admixture or an addition, namely:

(1) salt in butter or margarine;

(2) vitamins in food.

Every package, containing a food which is not pure by reason of any addition, admixture or deficiency shall be labeled with an adhesive label, which shall have the following declaration:

DECLARATION
THIS (a)................CONTAINS ADMIXTURE/ADDITION OF NOT MORE THAN (b)..............PER CENT OF (c)...

(1) Here insert the name of food.

(2) Here insert the quantity of admixture which may be present.

(3) Here insert the name of the admixture or the name of the ingredient which is deficient.

Where the content demands it, the words 'contains an admixture of' shall be replaced by the words 'contains an addition of' or 'is deficient in'.

Unless the vendor of a food containing an addition, admixture or deficiency, has reason to believe that the purchaser is able to read and understand the declaratory label, he shall give the purchaser, if asked, the information contained in the declaratory label by word of mouth at the time of sale.

Nothing contained in this rule shall be deemed to authorize any person to sell any article of food required under the Act or these rules to be sold in pure condition, otherwise than in its pure condition.

Nothing contained in the rule shall apply in the case of sweets, confectionery, biscuits, bakery products, processed fruits, aerated waters, vegetables and flavouring agents.

CHAPTER 15

FLAVOURING AGENTS, INSECTICIDES AND PESTICIDES

The use of *coumarin* and *dihydro coumarin* in any article of food is prohibited. Diethylene glycol, monoethyl ether and isopropyl alcohol shall not be used as solvent in flavours.

Food grade solvents: *Isopropyl* alcohol – Food grade may be used as solvent in Food Industry.

Monosodium glutamate may be added to meat products to a maximum limit of 500 ppm. It shall not be added to any food meant for infants below 12 months.

INSECTICIDES AND PESTICIDES

The amount of insecticide mentioned in column 2, on the foods mentioned in Column 3, shall not exceed the tolerance limit prescribed in column 4 of Table 15.1.

For the purposes of this rule:

(1) The expression "insecticide" shall have the meaning assigned to it in the Insecticide Act, 1968 46 of 1968;

(2) Unless otherwise stated-

(i) maximum levels are expressed in mg/kg on a whole product basis

(ii) all foods refer to raw agricultural products moving in commerce

Table 15.1: Restriction on the use of Insecticide and Pesticides

Sl. No.	Name of insecticide	Food	Tolerance limit mg/kg (p.p.m.)
1.	Aldrin, dieldrin (The limits apply to aldrin and dieldrin singly or in any combination and are expressed as dieldrin)	Food grains Milk and Milk products Fruits and Vegetables Meat Eggs	0.01 0.15 (on a fat basis) 0.01 0.02 0.01 (on a shell-free basis)
2.	Carbaryl	Food grains Okra and leafy vegetables Potatoes Other vegetables Cottonseed (whole) Maize cob (kernels)	1.5 10.0 0.2 5.0 1.0 1.0
3.	Chlordane (residue be measured as cis plus trans chlordane)	Food grains Milk and Milk products Vegetables Fruits Sugar beet	0.05 to 0.05 (on a fat basis) 0.2 0.1 0.3
4.	DDT (The limits apply to DDT, DDD and DDE singly or in any combination)	Milk and Milk Products Fruits and vegetables including potatoes Meat, poultry and fish	1.25 (on a fat basis) 3.5 7.0 (on whole product basis) 0.5 (on a shell-free basis)
5.	Diazinon	Food grains Vegetables	0.05 0.5
6.	Dichlorvos (content of dichloroace-taldehyde	Foodgrains Milled foodgrains	1.0 0.25

(contd...)

Sl. No.	Name of insecticide	Food	Tolerance limit mg/kg (p.p.m.)
	(DCA) be reported where possible	Vegetables Fruits	0.15 0.1
7.	Dicofol	Fruits and Vegetables Tea (dry manufactured)	5.0 5.0
8.	Dimethoate (residue to be determined as dimethoate and expressed as dimethoate)	Fruits and Vegetables	2.0
9.	Endosulfan (residues are measured and reported as total of endosulfan A and B endosulfan-sulphate)	Fruits and vege-tables Cottonseed Cottenseed oil (crude)	2.0 0.5 0.2 0.2
10.	Fenitrothion	Foodgrains Milled foodgrains Milk and milk products Fruits Vegetables Meat	0.02 0.005 0.05 (on a fat basis) 0.5 0.3 0.03
11.	Heptachlor (combined residues of heptachlor and its epoxide to be determined and expressed heptachlor)	Food grains Milled foodgrains Milk and milk products Vegetables	0.01 0.002 0.15 (on a fat basis) 0.05
12.	Hydrogen cyanide	Food grains Milled foodgrains	37.0 3.0
13.	Hydrogen phosphide	Foodgrains Milled foodgrains	0.05 0.01
14.	Inorganic bromide (determined and expres-sed as total bromide	Foodgrains Milled foodgrains Fruits	25.0 25.0 30.0

(contd...)

Sl. No.	Name of insecticide	Food	Tolerance limit mg/kg (p.p.m.)
	from all sources)	Dried fruits and spices	100.0
15.	Lindane	Foodgrains	0.25
		Milk and milk products	0.2 (on a fat basis)
		Fruits and vegetables	3.0
		Eggs	0.1 (on a shellfree basis)
		Meat and poultry	0.2 2.0 (on whole basis)
16.	Malathion (Malathion to be determined and expression as combined residues of malathion and malaoxon)	Foodgrains	4.0
		Milled foodgrains	1.0
		Fruits	4.0
		Vegetables	3.0
		Dried fruits	8.0
17.	Parathion (Combined residues of parathion and paraoxon to be determined and expressed as parathion)	Fruits and vegetables	0.5
18.	Parathion methyl (combined residues of parathion methyl and its oxygen analogue to be determined and	Fruits	0.2
		Vegetables	1.0
19.	Phosphamidon residues (expressed as the sum of the phosphamidon and its desethyl derivative)	Foodgrains	0.05
		Fruits and vegetables	0.2
20.	Pyrethrins (sum of pyrethrins I and II and other structurally related insecticidal ingredients of pyrethrum)	Foodgrains	1.5
		Milled foodgrains	0.5
		Fruits and vegetables	1.0

SOLVENT EXTORTED OILS AND EDIBLE FLOUR

Solvent-extracted oils means any vegetables oils obtained from oils-bearing material by the process of extraction by a solvent.

Conditions of Manufacturer, Stocks and Sale of Solvent-extracted Oil

The manufacturer, stock and sale of solvent-extracted oil shall comply with the following conditions, namely:

(1) The oil shall be manufactured only in factories licensed for the purpose under the Solvent extracted Oil, De-oiled Meal and Edible Flour (Control) Order, 1967 (hereinafter referred to as the said Order in this Part).

(2) The oil-bearing materials subject to the extraction process for the manufacture of solvent-extracted oil, and the solvent used in the said process, shall conform to the standards of quality laid down in sub-clauses (7) and (8) of Clause 9 of the said Order.

(3) Only such grades and varieties of solvent-extracted oil may be manufactured, stocked or sold for the purpose of direct human consumption as have been permitted in sub-clause (1) of Clause 9 of the said Order, and for the purpose of refining for direct human consumption or for use in the manufacture of vanaspati as have been permitted in sub-clause (2) of Clause 9 of the said Order and these oils shall conform to the appropriate standards of quality prescribed therein.

(4) The oils shall be packed and labeled in accordance with the requirements under Clause 11 of the said Order.

(5) The sale or movement of stocks of solvent-extracted oils other than of the "refined" grade, that is say, oil which has been neutralized, bleached and deodorized and conforms to the appropriate standards of quality of such oil, shall be governed by the provisions of sub-clause (3)

of clause 9 of the said order. Such oil shall be sold or moved by the producer directly to industrial users there of registered as such under the said Order and not to any other person or through any third party.

"Solvent-extracted edible flour" means the ground material obtained from specifically prepared de-boiled meal, that is, the residual material left over when oil is extracted by a solvent from oil-cake immediately following the single-pressing of good quality oilseeds.

Conditions of Manufacture, Stock and Sale of Solvent-extracted Edible Flour

The manufacture, stock and sale of solvent-extracted edible flour shall be subject to compliance with the following conditions, namely:

(1) The edible flour shall be manufactured only in factories liscensed for the purpose under the said Order.

(2) The de-oiled meal from which the edible flour is prepared and the solvent used in the extraction process, shall conform to standards of quality laid down in sub-clauses (6) and (8) of clause 9 of the said Order.

(3) Only such grades and qualities of edible flour may be manufactured as have been permitted in sub-clauses (6) of clause 9 of the said Order, and these shall conform to the appropriate standards of quality prescribed therein.

(4) The edible flour shall be packed and labeled in accordance with the requirements under Clause 11 of the said Order.

Manufacturers Distributors and Dealers to give Warranty

No manufacturer or distributor of, or dealer in, and article of food shell sell such article to any vendor unless he also gives a warranty in writing in the prescribed form about the nature and quality of such article to the vendor:

Provided that a bill, cash memorandum or invoice in respect of the sale of any article of food given by a manufacturer or distributor of, or dealer in, such article to the vendor there of shall be deemed to be a warranty given by such manufacturer, distributor or dealer under this section.

In this section, in sub-section (2) of section 19 and in section 20-A, the expression "distributor" shall include a commission agent.

Every vendor of an article of food shall, if so required, disclose to the Food Inspector the name, address and other particulars of the person from whom he purchased the article of food.

CHAPTER 16

PRESERVATIVES, POISONOUS METALS AND ANTI-OXIDANTS ETC.

"Preservative" means a substance which when added to capable of inhibiting, retanding or arresting the process of fermentation, acidification or other decomposition of food.

CLASSIFICATION OF PRESERVATIVES

Preservatives shall be divided into following classes:

(I) *Class I preservative shall be*:

(1) Common salt,
(2) Sugar,
(3) Dextrose,
(4) Glucose (Syrup),
(5) Wood smoke,
(6) Spices,
(7) Vinegar or acetic acid,
(8) Honey

Addition of Class I preservatives in any food is not restricted, unless otherwise provided in the rules.

The article of food to which a Class I preservative has been added conforms to the specifications laid down in Appendix 'B'of the Act.

(II) *Class II preservatives shall be*:

(1) Benzoic acid including salts thereof,
(2) Sulphurous acid including salts thereof,
(3) Nitrates or Nitrites of Sodium or Potassium in respect of food like ham, pickled meat,
(4) Sorbic acid including its sodium, potassium and calcium salts, propionates of calcium or sodium, lactic acid, and acid calcium phosphate,
(5) Nicin and
(6) Sodium and calcium propionate.

Use of more than One Class II Preservative

No person shall use in or upon a food more than one Class II preservative:

Wherein column (2) of Table 16.1 Rule 55 of the Act the use of more than one preservative has been allowed in the alternative, those preservatives may, notwithstanding anything contained in Rule 55, be used in combination with one or more alternatives, provided the quantity of each preservative so used does not exceed such number of parts out of those specified for that preservative in column (3) of the aforesaid table as may be worked out on the basis of the proportion in which such preservatives are combined.

Illustration: In the group of foods specified in Item 6 of Table 15.1, sulphur dioxide or Benzoic acid can be added in the proportion of 40 parts per million or 200 parts per million respectively. If both preservatives are used in combination and the proportion of sulphur dioxide is 20 parts per million the proportion of Benzoic acid shall not exceed the proportion of 100 parts per million.

USE OF CLASS II PRESERVATIVES

The use of Class II preservatives shall be restricted to the following group of foods in concentration not exceeding the proportions given in Table 16.1 against each:

Table 16.1: Preservatives Restricated in Food Articales

	Article of Food	Preservative	Parts per million
	1	2	3
1	Sausages and sausage meat containing raw meat cereals and condiments	Sulphur dioxide	450
2.	Fruit, fruit pulp or juice (not dried) for conversation into jam or crystallized glace or cured fruit or other products:		
	a. Cherries	Sulphur dioxide	3,000
	b. Strawberries and raspberries	Sulphur dioxide	2,000
	c. Other fruits	Sulphur dioxide	1,000
3.	Fruit juice concentrate	Sulphur dioxide	1,500
4.	Dried Fruits:		
	a. Apricots, peaches, apples, pears and other fruits	Sulphur dioxide	2,000
	b. Raisins and sultans	Sulphur dioxide	750
5.	Other non-alcoholic wines, squashes, crushes, fruit syrups, cordials, fruit juices and barley water to be used after dilution	Sulphur dioxide or Benzoic acid	350 350
6.	Jam, marmalade, preserve, canned cherry and fruit jelly	Sulphur dioxide or Benzoic acid	40 200
7.	Crystallized glace or cured fruit (including candided peel)	Sulphur dioxide	150
8.	Fruit and fruit pulp not otherwise specified in the schedule	Sulphur dioxide	350
9.	Sugar, glucose, gur and Khandsari	Sulphur dioxide	70
10.	Corn flour and such like starches	Sulphur dioxide	100
11.	Corn syrup	Sulphur dioxide	450
11-A	Canned *Rossogolla* (the cans shall be internally lacquered with sulphuriodixc resistant lacquer)	Sulphur dioxide	100
12.	Gelatine	Sulphur dioxide	1,000
13.	Beer	Sulphur dioxide	70
14.	Cider	Sulphur dioxide	200

(contd...)

	1	2	3
15.	Alcoholic wines	Sulphur dioxide	450
16.	Sweetened mineral water and sweetened ready-to-serve beverages	Sulphur dioxide or Benzoic acid	70 120
17.	Brewed ginger beer	Benzoic acid	120
18.	Coffee extract	Benzoic acid	450
19.	Pickles and chutneys made from fruit or vegetables	Benzoic acid or sulphur dioxide	250 100
20.	Tomato and other sauces	Benzoic acid	750
21.	Cooked pickled meat including ham and bacon	Sodium or Potassium nitrite (Calculated as sodium nitrite) or Commercial Saltpetre (calculated as sodium nitrate)	200 500
22.	Danish tinned caviar	Benzoic acid	50
23.	Dehydrated vegetables	Sulphur dioxide	2,000
24.	Tomato puree and paste	Benzoic acid	250
25.	Syrups and *sharbats*	Sulphur dioxide or Benzoic acid	600
26.	Dried ginger	Sulphur dioxide	2,000
27.	Hard boiled sugar confectionery	Sulphur dioxide	350
28.	Cheese or processed cheese	Sorbic acid including its Sodium, Potassium and Calcium salts (Calculated as Sorbid acid) or Nicin (Calculated as Sorbic acid)	1,000 1,000
29.	Flour confectionery	Sorbic acid or its Sodium salt	1,500
30.	Smoked fish (in wrappers)	Sorbic acid Only wrappers may be impregnated with Sorbic acid	
31.	Dry mixes of *Rasgollas*	Sulphur dioxide	100

Use of Class II Preservatives in Mixed Foods

In a mixture of two or more foods or groups of foods mentioned against each item in Table 16.1, the use of Class II preservative or preservatives shall be restricted to the limit up to which the use of such preservative or preservatives is permitted for the foods or groups of foods contained in such mixture.

Illustration – In the food specified in Item 23 of Table 16.1, sulphur dioxide can be added to dehydrated vegetables in the proportion of 2,000 parts per million. If this food is mixed with the specified in Items 24 given in the said table, that is to say tomato puree and paste, where benzoic acid is permitted to an extent of 250 p.p.m., then in the mixture containing equal parts of those two foods, the proportion of Sulphur dioxide and Benzoic acid, shall be 1,000 p.p.m., and 125 p.p.m. respectively.

Container of food which contains Preservative not to be marked "Pure"

The word "Pure" shall not be used on the liable of the container of any food which contains preservatives.

POISONOUS METALS

Chemicals described in monographs of the Indian Pharmacopoeia when used in foods, shall not contain poisonous metals beyond the limits specified in the appropriate monographs of the Indian Pharmacopoeia for the time being in force.

Notwithstanding the provisions of sub-rule (1); no article of food specified in Column 2 of Table 16.2 contain any metal specified in excess of the quantity specified in Column 3 of the said table:

ANTI-OXIDANTS, EMULSIFYING AND STABILIZING AND ANTIBAKING AGENTS

Definition of Anti-oxidant

Anti-oxidant means a substance which when added to food retards or prevents oxidative deterioration of food and does not include sugar, cereal, oils, flavours, herbs and spices.

Table 16.2: Use of Poisonous Metals

	Name of the Poisonous metal		Article of food	Parts per million by weight
	1		2	3
1.	Lead	:	(i) Beverages:	
			Concentrated soft drinks (but not including concentrates used in the manufacture of soft drinks)	0.5
			Fruit and vegetable juice (including tomato, juice, but not including lime juice and lemon juice)	1.0
			Concentrates used in the manufacture of soft drinks, lime juice and lemon juice	2.0
			(i-a) Baking powder	10
			(ii) Other foods:	
			Anhydrous dextrose and dextrose monophynrate, edible oils and fats, refined white sugar (sulphated ash content not exceeding 0.03 per cent)	0.5
			Ice cream, iced lollies and similar frozen confections	
			Canned fish, canned meat, edible gelatin, meat extracts and hydrolysed protein, dried or dehydrated vegetables (other than onions).	
			All types of sugar, syrup, invert sugar and direct consumption coloured sugars with sulphated ash content exceeding 1.0 per cent	
			Raw sugar except those sold for direct consumption or used for manufacturing purposes other than the manufacture or refined sugar	5.0
			Edible molasses, caramel, liquid and solid glucose and starch conversion products with a sulphated ash content exceeding 1.0 per cent	

(contd...)

1		2	3
		Cocoa Powder	5.0 one the dry fat free substance
		Yeast and yeast products	5.0 on the dry matter
		Tea, dehydrated onions, dried herbs and spices, flavourings, alginic acid, ginates agar, carrageen and similar products derived from seaweed.	100 on the dry matter
		Liquid pectin, chemicals not otherwise specified used as ingredients or in the preparation or processing of food	10.0 on the dry matter
		Food colouring other than caramel	10.0 on the dry colouring matter
		Solid pectin	50.0
		Hard boiled sugar confectionery	20
		(iii) Foods not specified	2.5
2.	Copper :	(i) Beverages:	
		Soft drinks excluding concentrates and Carbonated water	7.0
		Carbonated Water	1.5
		Concentrates for soft drinks	20.0
		(ii) Other foods:	
		Chicory-dried or roasted, coffee beans, flavourings, pectin-liquid	30.0
		Colouring	30.0 on the dry colouring matters

(contd...)

1			2	3
			Edible gelatin	30.0
			Tomato ketchup	50.0 on the dried total solids
			Yeast and yeast products	60.0 on the dry matter
			Cocoa Powder	70.0 on the fat free substance
			Tomato pureė, paste, power, juice and cocktails	100.0 on the dried tomato solids
			Tea	150.0
			Pectin-solid	300.0
			Hard boiled sugar confectionery	5.0
			(iii) Foods not specified	30.0
3.	Arsenic	:	(i) Milk	0.1
			(ii) Beverages	
			Soft drinks intended for consumption after dilution except carbonated water	0.5
			Carbonated water	0.25
			(iii) Preservative, anti-oxidants, emulsifying and stabilizing agents and synthetic food colours	3.0 on dry matter
			(iv) Other foods:	
			Ice cream, iced lollies and similar frozen confections	0.5
			Dehydrated onions, edible gelatin, liquid pectin	2.0
			Chicory-dried or roasted	4.0

(contd...)

1			2	3
			Dried herbs finings and clearing agents solid pectin-all grades spices	5.0
			Food colouring other than synthetic colouring	5.0 on dry colouring matter
			Hardware boiled sugar confectionery	1.0
			(v) Foods not specified	1.1
4.	Tin	:	(i) Processed and canned products	250.0
			(i-a) Hard boiled sugar confectionery	5.0
			(ii) Foods not specified	250.0
5.	Zinc	:	(i) Ready-to-drink beverages	5.0
			(ii) Edible gelatin	100.0
			(iii) Fruit products covered under the Fruit Products Order, 1955	50.0
			(iii-a) hard boiled sugar confectionery	5.0
			(iv) Foods not specified	50.0

No anti-oxidant other than lecithin, ascorbic acid and tocopnerol shall be added to any food:

The following anti-oxidants, not exceeding in concentration mentioned against each, may be added to edible oils fats, except ghee and butter, namely:

(1) Ethyl gallate

(2) Prophyl gallate

(3) Ocytyl gallate or mixture thereof : 0.01 per cent

(4) Dodecyl gallate

(5) Butylated hydroxytoluence (BHT), : 0.02 per cent

(6) Butylated hydroxyanisole (BHA) : 0.02 per cent

(7) Citric Acid

(8) Tartaric acid

(9) Gallic acid : 0.01 per cent

(10) Resin Guaiac : 0.05 per cent

Provided that dry mixes of Rasgollas and *Vadas* may contain butylated hydroxyanisole (BHA) not exceeding 0.02 per cent calculated on the basis of fat content:

Provided further that anti-oxidants permitted in Rule 59 may be used in permitted flavouring agents in concentration not exceeding 0.01 per cent:

Wherever butylated hydroxyanisole (BHA) is used in conjunction with the anti-oxidants mentioned at item Nos. 1 to 4 of the proceeding proviso, the quantity of the mixture shall not exceed the limit of 0.02 per cent:

Ghee and Butter may contain butylated hydroxyanisole (BHA) and butylated hydroxyanisole (BHT) either singly or in combination in a concentration not exceeding 0.02 per cent.

Use of anti-oxidants in Vitamin D preparation – Rule 59-A: Vitamin D preparation may contain anti-oxidants prescribed in Rule 59 not exceeding 0.08 per cent.

Definition of Emulsifying and Stabilizing Agents

"Emulsifying agents" and "stabilizing agents" mean substances which, when added to food, are capable of facilitating a uniform dispersion of oils and fats in aqueous media, or *vice versa,* and/ or stabilizing such emulsions and include the following namely:-

Agar, alginic acid, calcium and sodium alginates, carrageen, edible gums (such as guar, karaya, Arabic, carobean, furcellaran, traga canth, gum ghatti), dextrin, sorbitol, pectin, sodium and calcium pectate, sodium citrate, sodium phosphates, sodium phosphates, sodium tartarate, calcium lactate, lecithin, albumen, gelatin, quillaia, modified starches, hydrolysed proteins, monoglycerides or diglycerides of fatty acids, synthetic lecithin, prophyleneglycol stearatate, propyleneglycol alginate, methyl

ethyl cellulose, methyl cellulose, sodium carboxymethyl cellulose, stearyl tartaric acid, esters of monoglycerides and diglycerides of fatty acids, monostearin sodium sulphoacete, sorbitan estetars of fatty acids or in combination, poly-oxyethylene sorbiton monostearate sodium stearoyl-2-lactylate and calcium stearoyl-2-lactalyate and brominated vegetable oils.

Restribution on use of Emulsifying and Stabilizing Agent

No emulsifying or stabilizing agents shall be used in any food, except where the use of emulsifying or stabilizing agent is specifically permitted:

The following emulsifying or stabilizing agents shall not be used in milk and cream, namely: monoglycerides or diglycerides of fatty acids, synthetic lecithin, propyleneglycol stearate, propyleneglycol, alginate, methyl ethyl cellulose, methyl cellulose, sodium carboxymethyl cellulose stearyl tartaric acid, esters of monoglycerides and diglycerides of fatty acids, monostearin sodium sulphoacetate, sorbitan esters of fatty acids or in combination, and brominated vegetable oils.

Use of Starch Phosphate

Starch phosphate, a gum Arabic substitute, may be used in syrup, ice-cream powder, salad dressing and pudding to a maximum extent of 0.5 per cent.

Use of Emulsifying and Stabilizing Agents in Flavouring Agents

The emulsifying and stabilizing agents may be added to flavouring agents.

Restriction on Use of Anticaking Agents

No Anticaking agents shall be used in any food except where the use of anticaking agents is specifically permitted.

Table salt, onion powder, garlic powder and soup powder may contain aluminium silicate as anticaking agents to a maximum extent of 2 per cent.

PART III

CHAPTER 17

PROHIBITION AND REGULATION OF SALES AND CONDITIONS FOR SALE AND LICENCE

PROHIBITION AND REGULATION OF SALES

Sale of Certain Admixtures Prohibited

Notwithstanding the provisions of Rule 43 no person shall either by himself or by any servant or agent sell:

(1) Cream which has not been prepared exclusively from milk or which contains less than 25 per cent of milk fat,

(2) Milk which contains any added water,

(3) *Ghee* which contains any added matter not exclusively derived from milk fat,

(4) Skimmed milk (fat abstracted) as milk,

(5) A mixture of two or more edible oils as an edible oil,

(6) Vanaspati to which ghee or any other substance has been addcd

(7) Any article of food which contains any artificial sweetener, except where such artificial sweetener is permitted in accordance with the standard laid down in Appendix B of the Rule.

(8) Turmeric containing any foreign substance,

(9) Mixture of coffee and any other substance except chicory,

(10) *Dahi* or curd prepared from raw and untreated milk/ skimmed milk

(11) Milk or a milk product specified in Appendix B of the Rule containing a substance not found in milk, except as provided in the rules.

The Central Government may exempt any preparations made of soluble of extracts of coffee from the operation of this rule;

In respect of clause (e) a maximum tolerance of 5.0 red units in 1 cm. cell on Lovibond scale is permitted when the oil is tested for Boundouin test without dilution that is to say by shaking vigorously for 2 minutes, 5 ml. of the sample with 5 ml of hydrochloric acid (specific gravity 1.19) and 0.3 ml of 2 per cent alcoholic solution of furfural, and allowing to stand for 5 minutes:

Provided further that the prohibition in clause (e) shall remain inoperative [up to and including the 30th day of April, 1978] in respect of admixture of palmolein with groundnut oil, where,

(1) The proportion of groundnut oil in admixture is not less than ten per cent by weight;

(2) The admixture is processed and sold by the Department of Civil Supplies, Government of India or their authorized agents; and

(3) The palmolein and the groundnut oil in the admixture conform to the specifications laid down in the rules.

The clause (e) shall remain inoperative for a period of one year from the date of commencement of the Prevention of Food Adulteration Fourth Amendment Rules, 1977, in respect of admixture of imported rapeseed oil with mustard oil, where,

(1) The proportion of mustard oil in the admixture is not less than 20 per cent by weight;

(2) The admixture is processed and sold by the Department of Civil Supplies of the Government of India or the authorized agents of that Department; and

(3) The quality of imported rapeseed oil and the mustard oil in the admixture conform to the standards prescribed by the Central Government.

In respect of clause (e), maximum tolerance of 10 red unit 1 cm cell on lovibond scale is permitted when the oil is tested for Halphen's test without dilution, that is to say, by shaking 5 ml of the sample with 5 ml of sulphur solution one per cent (w/v) solution of sulphur in carbon disulfide mixed with equal volume of amyl alcohol, in a closed system test tube (250 × 25 cm) heating in hot water (70° C - 80°C) for a few minutes with occasional shaking until carbon disulfide is boiled off and the sample stops foaming and then placing the tube on saturated brine bath, capable of being regulated at 110°C-115°C for 2.5 hours.

No person in any State shall, with effect from such date as the State Government concerned may be notification in the Official Gazette specify in this behalf, sell or offer or expose for sale, or have in his possession for the purpose of sale, under any description or for use as an ingredient in the preparation of any article of food intended for sale

(1) *Kesari* gram (*Lathyrus sativus*) and its products.

(2) *Kesari daal* (*L. sativus*) and its products.

(3) *Kesari daal* flour (*L. sativus*) and its products.

(4) A mixture of *Kesari* gram (*L. sativus*) and Bengal-gram dal (Cicer arietinum) or any other gram,

(5) A mixture of *Kesari daal* (*L. sativus*) and Bengal-gram dal (Cicer Arietinum) or any other dal.

(6) A mixture of *Kesari daal* (*L. sativus*) flour and Bengal-gram (*Cicer arietinum*) flour or any other flour.

The equivalent of *Kesari* gram in some of the Indian languages are as follows:-

1. Assamese : *Khesari, Teora*
2. Bengali : *Khesari, Teora, Kassur, Batura*
3. Bihari : *Khesari, Teora, Kassur, Batura*
4. English : *Chikling vetch*
5. Gujarati : *Lang*
6. Hindi : *Khesari, Kassur, Kasari, Kassartiuri, Batura, Chapari, Dubia, Kansari, Kesori, Latri, Tinra, Tiuri, Kassor.*
7. Kannada : *Laki Bele, Kesari Bele*
8. Malyalam : *Kesari, Lanki, Vattu*
9. Tamil : *Muku*
10. Marathi : *Lakheri, Batri, Lakhi, Lang, Mutra, Teora, Batroli-ki-daal, lakh.*
11. Oriya : *Khesra, Khesari, Khesari daali.*
12. Persian : *Masang.*
13. Punjabi : *Kisari, Chural, Karas, Karil, Kasa, Kesari, Chapa.*
14. Sanskrit : *Sandika, Triput.*
15. Sindhi : *Matar*
16. Telugu : *Lamka*

In the absence of any amendment to Rule 44-A which totally prohibits the use of *kesari dal* in any form whatsoever in food-grains, direction by the central government issued under section 22-A of the Act to the effect that a mixture of *kesari dal* to the extent of a per cent might be permissible was held to be of no effect, since under the said section the government could only give direction for the implementation of the Rule and not for their contravention. Thus the direction issued by the government under section 22-A did not amend Rule 44-A.

Prohibition of use of Carbide Gas in Ripening of Fruits

No person shall sell or offer or expose for sale or have in his premises for the purpose of sale under any description, fruits which have been artificially ripened by use of acetylene gas, commonly known as carbide gas.

Restriction on Sale of Ghee having Less Reichert Value than that Specified for the Area where Such Ghee is Sold

The *ghee* having less Reichert value and a different standard for Butyro-refractometer reading at 40° C than that specified for the area in which it is imported for sale or storage shall not be sold or stored in that area except under the 'AGMARK' seal.

Such *ghee* may be (i) sold loose, after opening the 'AGMARK' sealed container, in quantities not exceeding two kilograms at a time, and (ii) used in the preparation of confectionery (including sweetmeats).

A person selling-

(1) Such *ghee* in the manner specified in sub-rule (1), and

(2) Confectionery (including sweetmeats) in the preparation of which such ghee is used, shall give a declaration in. Form VI-B (ref Fig 17.A) to the Food Inspector when a sample thereof is taken by him for analysis under Section 10 of the Act and also to a purchaser desiring to have the sample analysed under Section 12 of the Act.

If on analysis such sample is found to be conforming to the standards of quality prescribed for the area where it is alleged to have been produced, the *ghee* shall not be deemed to be adulterated by reason only that it does not conform to the standards of quality prescribed for the area where it is sold.

Restriction on Sale of *Til Oil* produced in Tripura, Assam and West Bengal

Til oil (Sesame oil) obtained from white, sesame seeds, grown in Tripura, Assam and West Bengal having different standard than those specified for til oil shall be sold in sealed containers bearing Agmark label. Where this til oil is sold or offered for sale without bearing an Agmark label the standard given for til oil shall apply.

FORM VI-B
(See Rule 44-B)
DECLARATION

I/We on behalf of ....
solemnly declare that the *ghee* sold by me/us/on behalf of
.... *ghee* used by me/us/on behalf of
....
.... in the preparation of
....
....
....

Confectionery (including sweetmeats)
is/was from a tin containing *ghee* of ....
number origin and having 'AGMARK' seal. The said tin pertains
to batch number .... and
was purchased by me/us/on behalf of ....
....
from Shri/Shrimati/Kumari/Sarvshri ....
as per invoice/cash/credit memo no ....
dated ....

Dated.............. *Signature of trader/traders*

Place ....

Figure 17.A: Specimen of Form VI-B Declaration

Restriction on Sale of *Carbia callosa* and Honey Dew

Carbia callosa and Honey dew shall be sold only in sealed containers bearing Agmark seal.

Restriction on Sale of Kangra Tea

Kangra tea shall be sold or offered for sale only after it is graded and marked in accordance with the provisions of the Agricultural Produce (Grading and Marking) Act, 1937 (1 of 1937) and the rules made thereunder.

Food Resembling but not Pure Honey not to be Marked Honey

No person shall use the word 'honey' or any word, mark illustration or device that suggests honey on the label or any package of, or in any advertisement for, any food that resembles honey but is not pure honey.

Sale or Use for Sale of Admixtures of *Ghee* or Butter Prohibited

No person shall sell or have in his possession for the purpose of sale or for use as an ingredient in the preparation of an article of food for sale a mixture of *ghee* or butter and any substance (a) prepared in imitation of or as a substitute for *ghee* or butter, or (b) consisting of or containing any oil or fat which does not conform to the definition of *ghee*:

Provided where a mixture prohibited by this rule is required for the preparation of an article of food, such mixture shall be made only at the time of the preparation of such article of food.

Addition of Artificial Sweetener to be Mentioned on the Label

Saccharin or any other artificial sweetener shall not be added to any article of food, except where the addition of such artificial sweetener is permitted in accordance with the standard laid down in Appendix 'B' of the Rule and where any artificial sweetener is added to any food, the container of such food shall be labeled with an adhesive declaratory label which shall be in the form given below:

"This .... (name of food) contains and admixture of.................(name of the artificial sweetener).

Every container or package of table salt containing aluminium silicate as anti-caking agent shall bear the following label namely:

TABLE SALT
(Contains permitted anti-caking agents)

Use of Flesh of Naturally Dead Animals or Fowls Prohibited

No person shall sell or use as an ingredient in the preparation of any article of food intended for sale, the flesh of any animal or fowl which has died on account of natural causes.

Sale of Permitted Food Colours

No person shall manufacture, sell, stock, distribute for sale coal-tar food colours or their mixtures or any preparation of such colours for use in or upon food except under a licence.

No person shall sell a permitted coal-tar dye, for use in or upon food unless its container carries a label stating the following particulars:

(1) The word "Food Colours",

(2) The chemical and the common or commercial name and colour index of the dye-stuff.

No person shall sell a mixture of permitted coal-tar dyes for use in or upon food unless its container carries a label stating the following particulars:

(1) The words "Food Colour Mixture",

(2) The chemical and the common or commercial name and colours index of the dye-stuffs contained in the mixture.

No person shall sell a preparation of permitted coal-tar dyes for use in or upon food unless its container carries a label stating the following particulars:

(1) The words "Food Colours Preparation";

(2) The name of the various ingredients used in the preparation.

The licence referred to in sub-rule (1) shall be issued by the licensing authority appointed under sub-rule (2) of Rule 50 and shall be subject to such conditions as the State Government may specify in this behalf.

The coal-tar dyes and their preparations or mixtures permitted for use in certain food shall be sold under only under Indian Standards Institution certification mark.

Sale of Insect-damaged Dry Fruits and Nuts

The dry fruits and nuts like raisins, currents, figs, cashewnuts, apricots, almonds may contain not more than 5 per cent of insect-damage fruits and nuts, by count.

The term 'nuts' is wide enough to include cashew-nuts. Originally the rules did not prescribe the standards of quality of purity in relation to dry fruits. That lacuna has, however, now even removed by the insertion of Rule 48-B. In the instant case there is no proof that the samples were taken from tins bearing the manufacturer's label guaranteeing purity of foods nor is there any such warranty in the invoice. It was however urged that tin box bore the imprint "good". But it merely contains a description of the goods. The word "good" is not a warranty as to quality. The accused is therefore not protected under section 19(2) of the Act, read with Rule 12-A of the Rules [Rule 48B and 12A and Section 19(2)].

CONDITIONS FOR SALE AND LICENCE

Condition for Sale

Every utensil or container used for manufacturing, preparing or containing any food or ingredient of food intended for sale shall be kept at all times in good order and repair and in a clean and sanitary condition. No such utensil or container shall be used for any other purpose.

No person shall use for manufacturing, preparing or storing any food or ingredient of food intended for sale, any utensil or container which is imperfectly enamelled or imperfectly tinned or which is made of such materials or is in such a state as to be likely to injure such food or render it noxious.

Every utensil or container containing any food or ingredient of food intended for sale shall at all times either provided with a tight-fitting cover or kept closed or covered by a properly fitting lid or by a close fitting cover or gauze net or other material of a texture sufficiently fine to protect the food completely from dust, dirt and flies and other insects.

No utensil or container used for the manufacture or preparation of or containing any food or ingredient of food intended for sale shall be kept in any place in which such utensil or container is likely by reason of impure air or dust or any offensive, noxious or deleterious gas or substance or any noxious or injurious emanations exhalation, or effluvium, to be contaminated and thereby render the food noxious.

An utensil or container made of the following materials or metals, when used in the preparation of food shall be deemed to render it unfit for human consumption:

(1) Containers which are rusty;

(2) Enamelled containers which have become chipped and rusty;

(3) Copper or brass containers which are not properly tinned; and

(4) Containers made of aluminium not conforming in chemical composition to IS: 20-1959 specification for Cast Aluminium and Aluminium Alloy for utensils or IS: 21-1959 specification for Wrought Aluminium and Aluminium Alloy for utensils;

Provided that utensils or containers made of copper though not properly tinned may be used for the preparation of sugar confectionery or essential oils and mere use of such utensils or containers shall not be deemed to render sugar, confectioners or essential oils unfit for human consumption.

No person shall sell compounded asafoetida exceeding one kilogram in weight except in a sealed container with a label.

No person shall sell Hingra without a label on its container upon which is printed a declaration in the form specified in Rule 42.

No person shall sell Titanium dioxide (food grade) except under Indian Standard Institution Certification Mark.

Conditions for Licence

No person shall manufacture, sell, stock, distribute or exhibit for sale any of the following articles of food, except under a licence:

(1) Milk of all classes and designations,

(2) Milk products, such as cream malai, curd, skimmed milk, curd, *chhena*, skimmed milk *chhenna*, cheese, processed, cheese ice-cream, milk-ices, condensed milk sweetened and unsweetened, condensed skimmed milk sweetened and unsweetened, milk powder, skimmed milk powder, partly skimmed milk powder, khoa, infant milk food, table butter, deshi butter,

(3) Edible animal body fats, such as beef fat, fat, mutton goat fat and lard,

(4) Edible vegetable oils,

(5) Edible fat including margarine,

(6) Pulses, gram, nuts, starches, sago, suji, such as maida, besan and articles made out of flour including bakery products,

(7) Non-alcoholic beverages such as carbonated water,

(8) Tea, coffee, cocoa and chicory,

(9) Spices and condiments, whole or ground, including saffron, curry powder, mustard seeds, asafetida and compounded asafetida,

(10) Sweetening agents such as sugars, honey, gur or jaggery,

(11) Flavouring agents, anti-oxidants, emulsifying and stabilizing agents, and preservatives permitted for use in food and container wrappers,

(12) Artificial sweeteners,

(13) Confectionery, sweetmeats and savoury,

(14) Ice candies,

(15) Edible Gelatin,

(16) Molasses,

(16) Copra

(17) Meat and Meat products, fish and fish products,

(18) Silver leaf for human consumption,

(19) Sweetened ice, thread candies and similar products,

(20) Sugar cane juice, fruit juice and sharbats (not covered under the Fruit Products Order, 1955):

Provided that the fruit products covered under Fruit Product Order, 1955, solvent extracted oils and edible flour covered under the Solvent Extracted Oils, De-oiled Meal and Edible Flour (Control) Order, 1967, and Vanaspati covered under the Vegetable Oil Products Control Order 1947, shall be exempted from the above rule,

(21) Prepared foods or ready-to-serve food.

One licence may be issued by the licensing authority for one or more articles of food.

The name and address of the Director or Manager, as the case may be, nominated by the company under Rule 12-B shall be mentioned in the licence.

The State Government or the local authority shall appoint licensing authorities.

A licensing authority may with the approval of the State Government or the local Authority by an order in writing delegate the power to sign licences and such other powers as may be specified in the order to any other person under his control.

If articles of food are manufactured, stored or exhibited for sale at more than one place, separate application shall be made, and a separate licence shall be issued, in respect of each place.

This shall not apply to itinerant vendors who have no specified place of business and who will be licensed to conduct business in a particular area within the jurisdiction of the licensing authority for the grant of a licence:

Before granting a licence for manufacture, stock or exhibition of any of the articles of food in respect of which a licence is required, the licensing authority shall respect the premises and satisfy itself that it is free from sanitary defects. The applicant for the licence shall have to make such alteration in the premises as may be required by licensing authority for the grant of a licence:

Provided that the licensing authority may, for reasons to be recorded in writing, refuse to grant a licence, if it is satisfied that it is necessary to do so in the interest of public health.

Proprietors of hotels, restaurants and other food stalls (including mobile and itinerant food stall who sell or expose for sale savouries, sweets or other articles of food shall put up a notice board containing separate lists of the articles which have been cooked in ghee, edible oil, vanaspati and other fats for the information of the intending purchasers.

No licence shall employ in his work any person who as suffering from infection, contagious or loathsome disease.

No person shall manufacture, store or expose for sale or permit the sale of any article of food in and premises not effectively separated to the satisfaction of the licensing authority from any privy, urinal, sullage, drain or place of storage of foul and waste matter.

All vessels used for the storage or manufacture of the articles intended for sale shall have proper cover to avoid contamination.

Every manufacturer (including *ghani* operator) or whole sale dealer in butter, ghee, vanaspati, edible oils and other fats shall maintain a register showing the quantity manufactured, received or sold and the designation of each consignment of the substances sent out from his manufactory or place of business, and shall present such register for inspection whenever required to do so by the licensing authority.

An itinerant vendor granted a licence under these rules, shall carry a metallic badge on his arm showing clearly the licence number, the nature of articles for the sale of which the licence has been granted, his name and address and the name and address of the owner if any, for whom he is working. His containers of food and the vehicle shall also be similarly marked. In addition to the metallic badge the vendor shall if so required by the State Government or the local authority, carry an identify card with his photograph and the number of the licence. The identify card shall be renewed every year:

Provided that the whole-time employees of the companies shall not be treated as itinerant vendors for the purposes of carrying a metallic badge on their arms of obtaining separate licence if an identify card containing particulars, of the valid municipal licence is carried by them.

The nature of articles of food for the sale of which a licence is required under these rules shall be mentioned in the application for licence. Any objectionable, ambiguous or misleading trade name shall not be approved by the licensing authority.

Every licence who sells any food, shall display a notice board containing the nature of articles which he is exposing or offering for sale.

CHAPTER 18

FOOD POISONING, OFFENCES, WARRANTY, PUNISHMENT AND ALLIED ISSUES

FOOD POISONING AND OFFENCES

The Central Government or the State Government may, by notification in the Official Gazette, require medical practitioners carrying on their profession in any local area specified in the notification to report all occurrences of food poisoning coming within their cognize to such officer as may be specified in the notification.

Penalties

Subject to the provisions of sub-section (1A) if any person:

(1) whether by himself or by any other person on his behalf, imports into India or manufacturers for sale, or stores, sells or distributes any article of food:

- (i) which is adulterated within the meaning of sub-clause (m) of clause (ia) or Section 2 or misbranded within the meaning of clause (ix) of that section or the sale of which is prohibited under any provision of this Act or any rule made thereunder or by an order of the Food (Health) Authority;
- (ii) other than an article of food referred to in sub-clause (i), in contravention of any of the provisions of this Act or of any rule made thereunder; or

(2) whether by himself or by any other person on his behalf, imports into India or manufacturers for sale, or stores, sells or distributes any adulterant which is not injurious to health; or

(3) prevents a Food Inspector from taking a sample as authorized by this Act; or

(4) prevents a Food Inspector from exercising any other power conferred on him by or under this Act; or

(5) being a manufacturer of an article of food, has in his possession or in any of the premises occupied by him, any adulterant which is not injurious to health; or

(6) uses any report or certificate of a test or analysis made by the Director of the Central Food Laboratory or by a public analyst or any extract thereof for the purposes of advertising any article of food; or

(7) whether by himself or by any other person on his behalf, gives to the vendor a false warranty in writing in respect of any article of food sold by him,

he shall, in addition to the penalty to which he may be liable under the provisions of Section 6, be punishable with imprisonment for a term which shall not be less than six months but which may extend to three years, and with fine which shall not be less than one thousand rupees.

(1) If the offence is under sub-clause (i) of clause (a) and is with respect to an article of food, being primary food, which is adulterated due to human agency or is with respect to an article of food which is misbranded within the meaning of sub-clause (k) of clause (ix) of Section 2; or

(2) If the offence is under sub-clause (ii) of clause (a), but not but not being an offence with respect to the contravention of any rule made under clause (a) or clause

(g) of sub-section (1A) of section 23 or under clause (b) of sub-section (2) of section 24.

The court may, for any adequate and special reasons to be mentioned in the judgment, impose a sentence of imprisonment for a term which shall not be less than three months but which may extend to two years, and with fine which shall not be less than five hundred rupees.

If the offence is under sub-clause (ii) of clause (a) and is with respect to the contravention of any rule made under clause (a) or clause (g) of sub-section (1-A) of Section 23 or under clause (b) of sub-section (2) of Section 24, the court may, for any adequate and special reasons to be mentioned in the judgment, impose a sentence of imprisonment for a term which may extend to three months and with fine which may extend to five hundred rupees.

If any person whether by himself or by any other person on his behalf, imports into India or manufacturers for sale, or stores, sells or distributes, -

(1) Any article of food which is adulterated within the meaning of any of the sub-clause (e) to (1) (both inclusive) of clause (ia) of Section 2; or

(2) Any adulterant which is injurious to health,

he shall, in addition to the penalty to which he may be liable under the provisions of Section 6, be punishable with imprisonment for a term which shall not be less than one year but which may extend to six years and with fine which shall not be less than two thousand rupees:

If such article of food or adulterant, when consumed by any person is likely to cause his death or is likely to cause such harm on his body as would amount to grievous hurt within the meaning of section 320 of the Indian Penal Code (45 of 1860), he shall be punishable with imprisonment for a term which shall not be less than three years but which may extend to term of life and with fine which shall not be less than five thousand rupees.

If any person in whose safe custody any article of food has been kept under sub-section (4) of section 10, tampers or in any other manner interferes with such article, he shall be punishable with imprisonment for a term which shall not be less than six months but which may extend to two years and with fine which shall not be less than one thousand rupees.

If any person in whose safe custody any article of food has been kept under sub-section (4) of section 10, sells or distributes such article which is found by the magistrate before whom it is produced to be adulterant within the meaning of sub-clause (h) of clause (ia) of section 2 and which, when consumed by any person, is likely to cause his death or is likely to cause such harm on his body as would amount to grievous hurt within the meaning of section 320 of the Indian Penal Code (45 of 1860), then, notwithstanding anything contained in sub-section (1-AA), he shall be punishable with imprisonment for a term which shall not be less than three years but which may extend to term of life and with fine which shall not be than five thousand rupees.

If any person contravenes the provisions of Section 14 or Section 14A, he shall be punishable with imprisonment for a term which may extend to six months and with fine which shall not be less than five hundred rupees.

If any person convicted of an offence under this Act commits a like offence afterwards, then, without prejudice to the provisions of sub-section (2), the court, before which the second or subsequent conviction takes place, may order the cancellation of the licence, if any , granted to him under this Act and thereupon such licence shall, notwithstanding anything contained in this Act, or in the rules made thereunder, stand cancelled.

If any person convicted of an offence under this Act commits a like offence afterwards it shall be lawful for the court before which the second or subsequent conviction takes place to cause the offender's name and place of residence, the offence and the penalty imposed to be published at the offender's expense in such newspapers or in such other manner as the court may direct. The expenses of such publication shall be deemed to be part of the cost attending the conviction and shall be recoverable in the same manner as a fine.

Provided further that when at the commencement of or in the course of a summary trial under this section, it appears to be Magistrate that the nature of the case is such that a sentence of imprisonment of a term exceeding one year may have to be passed or that it is, for and other reason, undesirable to try the case summarily, the Magistrate shall after hearing the parties record an order to that effect and thereafter recall any witness who may have been examined and proceed to hear or rehear the case in the manner provided by the said Code.

OFFENCES BY COMPANIES

Where an offence under this Act has been committed by a company –

(1)(i) The person, if any, who has been nominated under sub-section (2) to be in charge of, and responsible to, the company for the conduct of the business of the company (hereinafter) in this section referred to as the person responsible), or

(ii) Where no person has been so nominated every person who at the time the offence was committed was in charge of, and was responsible to, the company for the conduct of the business of the company; and

(2) The company,

shall be deemed to be guilty of the offence and shall be liable to be proceeded against and punished accordingly:

Nothing contained in this sub-section shall render any, such person liable to any punishment provided in this Act if he proves that the offence was committed without his knowledge and that he exercised all due diligence to prevent the commission of such offence.

Any company may, by order in writing, authorize any of its directors or managers (such manager being employed mainly in a managerial or supervisory capacity) to exercise all such powers and take all such steps as may be necessary or expedient to prevent the commission by the company of any offence under this Act and may give notice to the Local (Health) Authority, in such form and in such manner as may be prescribed, that it has nominated such director or manager as the person responsible, along with the written consent of such director or manager for being so nominated.

Where a company has different establishments or branches or different units in any establishment or branch, different persons may be nominated under this sub-section in relation to different establishments or branches or units and the person nominated in relation to any establishment, branch or unit shall be deemed to be the person responsible in respect of such establishment, branch or unit.

The person nominated under sub-section (2) shall, until -

(1) further notice canceling such nomination is received from the company by the Local (Health) Authority; or

(2) he cases to be a director or, as the case may be, manager of the company; or

(3) he makes a request in writing to the Local (Health) Authority, under intimation to the company, to cancel the nomination (which request shall be complied with by the Local (Health) Authority.

Whichever is the earliest, continue to be the person responsible;

Where such person cases to be a director or, as the case may be, manager of the company, he shall intimate the fact of such cesser to the Local (Health) Authority;

Where such person makes a request under clause (iii) the Local (Health) Authority shall not cancel such nomination with effect from a date earlier than the date on which the request is made.

Notwithstanding anything contained in the foregoing sub-section where an offence under this Act has been committed by a company and it is proved that the offence has been committed with the consent or connivance of, or is attributable to, any neglect on the part of, any director, manager, secretary or other officer of the company, not being a person nominated under sub-section (2) such director, manager, secretary or other officer shall also be deemed to be guilty of that offence and shall be liable to be proceeded against and punished accordingly.

For the purposes of this section:

(1) "Company" means any body corporate and includes a firm or other association of individuals;

(2) "Director' in relation to a firm, means a partner in the firm; and

(3) "Manager" in relation to a company engaged in hotel industry, includes the person in charge of the catering department of any hotel managed or run by it.

FORFEITURE OF PROPERTY

Where any person has been convicted under this Act for the contravention of any of the provisions of this Act or of any rule thereunder, the article of food in respect of which the contravention has been committed may be forfeited to the Government.

Where the court is satisfied that the article of food is capable of being made to conform to prescribed standard formula consumption after reprocessing, the court may order the article of food to be returned to the owner, on his executing a bond with or without sureties, for being sold, subject to the other provisions of this Act, after reprocessing under the supervision of such officer as may be specified therein.

Defences which may or may not be allowed in Prosecutions under this Act (S. 19)

(1) It shall be no defence in a prosecution for an offence pertaining – to the sale of any adulterated or misbranded

article of food to allege merely that the vendor was ignorant of the nature, substance or quality of the food sold by him or that the purchaser having purchased any article for analysis was not prejudiced by the sale.

(2) A vendor shall not deemed to have committed an offence pertaining to the sale of any adulterated or misbranded article of food if he proves -

(a) That he purchased the article of food –

(i) In a case where a licence is prescribed for the sale thereof, from a duly licensed manufacturer, distributor or dealer;

(ii) In any other case, from any manufacturer, distributor or dealer;

(b) That the article of food while in his possession was properly stored and that he sold it in the same state as he purchased it.

(3) Any person by whom a warranty as is referred to in section 14 is alleged to have been given shall be entitled to appear at the hearing and give evidence.

Power of Court to Implead Manufacturer etc. (S. 20A)

Where at any time during the trial of any offence under this Act alleged to have been committed by any person, not being the manufacturer, distributor or dealer of any article of food, the court is satisfied, on the evidence adduced before it, that such manufacturer, distributor or dealer is also concerned with that offence, then the court may, notwithstanding anything contained in sub-section (3) of section 319 of the Code of Criminal Procedure, 1973 (2 of 1974) or in section 20 proceed against him as though a prosecution had been instituted against him under section 20.

Magistrate's Power to Impose Enhanced Penalties (S 21)

Notwithstanding anything contained in section 29 of the Code of Criminal Procedure, 1973 (2 of 1974), it shall be lawful for any Metropolitan Magistrate or any Judicial Magistrate of the first class, any sentence authorized by this Act, except a sentence of imprisonment for life or for a term exceeding six years, in excess of his powers under the said section.

Protection of Action taken in Good Faith

No suit, prosecution or other legal proceedings shall lie against any person for anything which is in good faith done or intended to be done under this Act.

Power of Central Government to give Directions (S 22A)

The Central Government any give such directions as it may deem necessary to a State Government regarding the carrying into execution of all or any of the provisions of this Act and the State Government shall comply with such directions.

Power of the Central Government to make Rules

The Central Government may, after consultation with the Committee and after previous publication by notification in the Official Gazette, make rules to carry out the provisions of this Act:

Provided that consultation with the Committee may be dispensed with if the Central Government is of the opinion that circumstances have arisen which render it necessary to make rules without such consultation, but in such a case, the Committee shall be consulted within six months of the making of the rules and the Central Government shall take into consideration any suggestions which the Committee may make in relation to the amendment of the said rules.

In particular and without prejudice to the generality of the foregoing power such rules may provide for all or any of the following matters, namely:

(1) Specifying the articles of food or classes of food for the import of which a licence is required and prescribing the form and conditions of such licence the authority

empowered to issue the same the fees payable therefore, the deposit of any sum as security for the performance of the conditions of the licence and the circumstances under which such licence or security may be cancelled or forfeited:

(2) Defining the standards of quality for, and fixing the limits of variability permissible in respect of, any article of food;

(3) Laying down special provisions for imposing rigorous control over the production, distribution and sale of any article or class of articles of food which the Central Government may, by notification in the Official Gazette, specify in this behalf including registration of the premises where they are manufactured, maintenance of the premises in a sanitary condition and maintenance of the healthy state of human beings associated with the production distribution and sale of such article or class of articles;

(4) Restricting the packing and labeling of any article of food and the design of any such package or label with a view to preventing the public or the purchaser being deceived or misled as to the character quality or quantity of the article or to preventing adulteration;

(5) Defining the qualifications, powers and duties of food inspectors and public analysis;

(6) Defining the laboratories where samples of articles of food or adulterants may be analysed by public analysis under this act;

(7) Prohibiting the sale or defining the conditions of sale or any substance which may be injurious to health when used as food or restricting in any manner its use as an ingredient in the manufacture of any article of food or regulating by the issue of licences the manufacture or sale of any article of food;

(8) Defining the conditions of sale or conditions for licence of sale of any article of food in the interest of public health;

(9) Specifying the manner in which containers for samples of food purchased for analysis shall be sealed up or fastened up;

(10) Defining the methods of analysis;

(11) Specifying a list of permissible, preservatives, other than common salt and sugar which alone shall be used in preserved fruits, vegetables or their products or any other article of food as well as the maximum amounts of each preservative;

(12) Specifying the colouring matter and the maximum quantities thereof which may be used in any article of food;

(13) Providing for the exemption from this Act or of any requirements contained therein and subject to such conditions, if any, as may be specified, of any articles or class or articles of food;

(14) Prohibiting or regulating the manufacture, transport or sale of any article known to be used as an adulterant of food;

(15) Prohibiting or regulating –

(i) The addition of any water, or other diluent or adulterant to any article of food;

(ii) The abstraction of any ingredient from any article of food;

(iii) The sale of any article of food to which such addition or from which such abstraction has been made or which has been otherwise artificially treated;

(iv) The mixing of two or more articles of food which are similar in nature or appearance.

(16) Providing for the destruction of such articles of food as are not in accordance with the provisions of this Act or of the rules made thereunder.

Every rule made by the Central Government under this Act shall be laid as soon as may be after it is made before each House of Parliament while it is in session for a total period of thirty days which may be comprised in one session or in two or more successive session and if before the expiry of the session immediately following the session or the successive sessions aforesaid both Houses agree in making any modification in the rule of both Houses agree that the rule should not be made, the rule shall thereafter have effect only in such modified form or be of no effect, as the case may be; so however, that any such modification or annulment shall be without prejudice to the validity of anything previously done under that rule.

POWER OF THE STATE GOVERNMENT

(1) The State Government may, after consultation with the Committee and subject to the condition of previous publication, make rules for the purpose of giving effect to the provisions of this act in matters not falling within the purview of section 23.

(2) In particular, and without prejudice to the generality of the foregoing power, rules may -

(a) Define the powers and duties of the Food (Health) Authority and Local Authority and Local (Health) Authority under this Act;

(b) Prescribe the forms of licences for the manufacture for sale, for the storage, for the sale and for the distribution of articles of food or any specified article of food or class of articles of food, the form of application for such licences, the conditions subject to which such licences may be issued, the authority empowered to issue the same, the fees payable therefore, the deposit of any sum as security for the performance of the conditions of the licences and the circumstances under which such licences or security may be suspended, cancelled or forfeited;

(c) Direct a fee to be paid for analyzing any article of food or for any matter for which a fee may be prescribed under this act:

(d) Direct that the whole or any part of the fines imposed under this Act shall be paid to a local authority on realization;

(e) Provide for the delegation of the powers and functions conferred by this Act on the State Government or the Food (Health) Authority to subordinate authorities or to local authorities.

(3) All rules made by the State Governments under this Act shall, as soon as possible after they are made, be laid before the respective State Legislatures.

REPEAL AND SAVING

If, immediately before the commencement of this Act, there is force in any State to which this Act extends any law corresponding to this Act, that corresponding law shall upon such commencement stand repealed.

Notwithstanding the repeal by this Act of any corresponding law, all rules, regulations and bye-laws relating to the prevention of adulteration of Food, made under such corresponding law and in force immediately before the commencement of this Act shall except where and so far as they are inconsistent with or repugnant to the provisions of this Act, continue in force until altered, amended repealed by rules made under this Act.

WARRANTY

According to Section the Manufactures, Distributors and Dealers to give Warranty

No manufacturer of distributor of, or dealer in, and article of food shall sell such article to any vendor unless he also gives a warranty in writing in the prescribed from about the nature and quality of such article to the vendror:

> Provided that a bill, cash memorandum or invoice in respect of the sale of any article of food given by a manufacturer or distributor of, or dealer in, such article to the vendor thereof shall be deemed to be a warranty given by such manufacutrer, distributor or dealer under the section.

In this section, in sub-section (2) of Section 19 and in Section 20A, the expression "disributor" shall include a commission agent.

According to **Section 14A** every vendor of an article of food shall, if so required, disclose to the Food Inspector the name, address and other particulars of the person from whom he purchased the article of food.

Every manufacturer, distributor or dealer selling an article of food to a vendor shall give either separately or in the bill, cash memo or label, a warranty in Form VI-A. (Ref. Fig. 17F`

Rule 12-A provides that every manufacturer, distributor or dealer selling an article of food to a vendor shall give either separately or in the bill, cash memo or label a warranty in Form VI-A. As Rule 12-A was there prior to the insertion of proviso to Section 14 and as the proviso does not say that the cash bill should be in accordance with the warranty and there is no question of deeming it as a warranty under the proviso to section 14, if a bill is given under Rule 12-A it by itself becomes a warranty or it may be done under proviso to section 14.

When the proviso to Rule 12-A of the Prevention of Food Adulteration Rules expressly says that no warranty in Form VI-A shall be necessary in certain eventualities, it would be rewriting the rule to infer that nevertheless the same thing must exist in the label or the cash memo. If the words in the warranty can reasonably be interpreted to have the same effect as certifying the nature, substance and quality of an article of food, the warranty will fall within the proviso. The act is of wide application and millions of small traders have to comply with the provisions of the Act and the Rules. If the object underlying the Act can be achieved, without disorganizing the trade, by giving a reasonable interpretation to Rule 12-A it is the court's duty to do so. The object of the Art is not defeated if the traders use ordinary language of the trade or popular language in warranties.

A cash memo may also serve the purpose of a warranty if it was in the Form VI-A. In the instant case the cash memo was written as given in Fiagure 18.A.:

CASH MEMO

Quantity	Description	Rate	Per	Amount
1	C/C Comela Milk	C70	Cash	Rs. 70.00
2.				
3.				
4.				
5.				
6.				
7				
8.				
9.				

Figure 18A: Specimen of a Cash Memo

There is not a whisper of any warranty in it.

Rule 12-A provides that the vendor shall give a warranty either separately or in the bill or cash memo or in label in Form VI-A. In the instant case the label on the tin of the condensed milk is as follows:

> "Comela" – Full Cream sweetened condensed milk made on formula of Holland Product.
>
> 'Comela Brand' – The contents of the tin are scientifically preserved pure and produced from healthy cow's milk. Comela full cream condensed milk easily digestible and are ideal food for babies.
>
> Special care is taken to maintain freshness-prepared by Kwality Dairy."

The Supreme Court held that this label contains no warranty of the kind referred to Rule 12-A. Further held that this was not even in the form given for a label prescribed for "Sweetened Condensed milk" which under Rule 42-B was to be as follows:

CONDENSED FULL CREAM MILK

(SWEETENED)

This tin contains the equivalent of .... liters

of milk with sugar added.

It may be that the inscription on the prescribed label, "This tin contains an equivalent of....................liters of milk with sugar added" was meant to serve the purpose of a warranty though it is couched in different language. For, it may be possible to ascertain by reference to standard tables the quantity of milk sold and fat from the quantity of milk condensed in the tin. It would not be possible even to do this on the basis of the particulars given on the labels borne on the tins which were taken as samples by the Food Inspector from the accused vendor. The label is therefore of little assistance to accused vendor.

Form of Warranty (Form VI-A)

Condensed milk sold by the accused found to be far below the prescribed standard of quality. Absence of warranty in prescribed form - neither label which was not in prescribed form nor cash memo containing warranty that food was same in nature, substance and quality as demanded by the vendor. The accused had failed to establish defence under section 19(2) read with Rule 12-A and Form VI-A and the fact that the accused sold article in same state as they purchased them was not by itself sufficient to absolve them.

Condensed milk sold by the accused found to be far below the prescribed standard of quality. There was absence of warranty in prescribed form. Neither label which was also not in prescribed form nor cash memo containing any warranty that food was same in nature, substance and quality as demanded by vendor was present.

Held that the accused had failed to establish the defence under section 19(2) read with Rule 12-A and Form VI-A. (Ref Fig 18.B).

If the warranty is not contained in a label or cash memo the warranty must be in Form VI-A. Words, "Quality is up to the mark" in cash memo mean that the quality of the article is up to the standard required by the Act and vendee. Quality in this context could include nature and substance, because name of the article is given in cash memo.

FORM VI-A

(See Rule 12-A)

FORM OF WARRANTY

Invoice No.______________

From__________________

To____________________

Place__________

Date__________

Date of Sale	Nature and quality of article	Batch No. or Code No.	Quantity	Price
1	2	2A	3	4

I/We hereby certify that food/foods mentioned in this invoice is/are warranted to be of the nature and quality which it/these purports/purport to be.

....

Signature of manufacturer,

Distributor or dealer

Licence N.........

(wherever applicable)

Figure-18B: Specimen of Form VI-A Form of Warranty

Warranty must be in writing and in the prescribed form. A label or cash memo cannot be termed as a warranty unless it falls within proviso to Rule 12-A.

What the rule making authority has done by the proviso to Rule 12-A is to relax the rigour or rule insisting upon obtaining a warranty by the vendor in Form VI-A. But that would not dispense with the necessity of obtaining a warranty certifying that the article of food sold is the same in nature, substance and quality as demanded by the vendor. The idea behind the proviso is only to save the vendors from the inconvenience of obtaining a separate warranty in Form VI-A but that does not mean that the warranty on the label or the cash memo need not certify that food contained in package or mentioned in the cash memo is the same in nature, substance and quality as demanded by the vendor. The word "quality" cannot convey the idea denoted by "nature" or "substance". It is incorrect to say that when quality alone was certified to be up to the mark that it would imply that the "nature" or "substance" of the article was warranted to be the same as demanded by the vendee.

CONSENT

(1) A company may inform the Local (Health) Authority of the concerned local area, by notice in duplicate, in Form VIII (Ref. Fig. 18C) containing the name and address of the director or Manager, who has been nominated by it under sub-section (2) of Section 17 of the Act to be in charge of, and responsible to, the company for the conduct for the conduct of the business of the company or any establishment, branch or unit thereof;

No such nomination shall be valid unless the Director or Manager who has been so nominated, gives his consent in writing and has affixed his signature, in Form VIII in duplicate in token of such consent.

(2) The Local (Health) Authority shall sign and return one copy of the notice in Form VIII to the company to signify

FORM VIII

(See Rule 12-B)

NOMINATION OF PERSONS BY A COMPANY

Notice is hereby given that Shri/Smt .... Director/Manager of the .... (name of the company) has been nominated by the company by a Resolution passed at their meeting held on............. at.............to be in charge of, and responsible to, the said company for the conduct of the business of the said company or.............establishment/branch/unit thereof and authorized to exercise all such powers and take all such steps as may be necessary or expedient to prevent the commission by the said company of any offence under the Prevention of Food Adulteration Act, 1954.

A certified copy of the said Resolution is enclosed.

Place................. Managing Director/Secretary

Date.................. ....

(name of the company)

Note:- Score out the portion which is not applicable.

I accept the above nomination in pursuance of sub-section (2) of Section 17 of the Prevention of Food Adulteration Act, 1954 and Rule 12-B of the rules made thereunder.

Place................. Managing Director/Secretary

Date.................. ....

(name of the company)

I hereby acknowledge receipt of the above nomination.

Place................. Signature of the Local (Health)

Date.................. Authority

Figure 18C: Specimen of Form VIII: Nomination of Persons by a Company

the receipt of the nomination and retain the second copy in his office for record.

Every vendor of an article of food shall disclose the name and address of the Director or Manager, as the case may be, nominated in Form VIII (Ref Fig. 18C) under Rule 12-B to a purchaser who informs such vendor of his intention of purchasing any such article from him for analysis by a public analyst under Section 12 of the Act.

Power of Food Inspector to Deal with Carriers of Disease Handling Food

Where the food inspector is of the opinion that any person engaged in selling or manufacturing any article of food is suffering from or harbouring the germs of any infectious disease, he may examine or cause to be examined such person;

Where such person is a female above the age of eight years she shall be examined by a woman duly authorized by the food inspector;

If on such examination the food inspector finds that such person is suffering from any such disease, he may by order in writing direct such person not to take part in selling or manufacturing any article of food.

The standard of qualities of the articles of food have been fixed by the government under the provisions of the Act after due deliberation and after consulting a committee of competent men. It is for them to give due allowance for probable errors before fixing a standard. The government may have done it also. There is no reason to assume otherwise. Therefore the conclusion is that for an article of food when a standard has been fixed under the Act, it has to be observed in every detail.

An Item of Food is Either Adulterated or Not

The statute does not admit of a via media position on this question. The government framed the rules defining the standard of quality for and fixing the limits of variability permissible in respect of any article of food. The standard fixed under the Act is one that is certain. If it is varied to a certain extent, the certainty of general standard would be replaced by the vagaries of a fluctuating standard.

An article of food is deemed to be adulterated if the quality of purity of the article falls below the prescribed standard of its constituents are present in quantities which are in excess of the prescribed limits of variability. The words used are "prescribed standards" and not "prescribed standard". *Prima facie*, it would therefore appear that if the article of food does not conform to any of the prescribed standards, it will come within its mischief. Even if all the tests prescribed are not followed, it would not necessarily mean that the court could not conclude that a particular article of food is adulterated if it does not conform to one or more of the standards prescribed.

PUNISHMENT AND ALLIED ISSUES

Legislative History of Section 16(1)

(1) Section 16(1) of the Prevention of Food Adulteration Act, 1954 (as amended by act 49 of 1964) the amending clause as is patent, has made the punishment conjunctive, that is to say, the punishment shall always take the form of imprisonment with a fine super-added. That this is the legislative intent is gatherable from the very wording of the section of the Act and that cannot be deemed to have been taken away and the punishment made disjunctive by the proviso. The legislative intent can be gauged further from the corresponding provision in the old section, that is section 16(1)(g) of the Prevention of Food Adulteration Act, 1954 as it stood before its amendment in 1964.

(2) The intention of the legislature is manifest when it provided minimum penalty for the offence for adulteration in food. The penalty clause was made more severe and drastic through amendment. In the background of the legislative history of this provision when the legislature provided a

strong arm to the government machinery to curb the social menance of adulteration, it cannot be assumed even remotely that the proviso could have so much dilutory effect on the penalty clause of section 16(1) of the Act as to eliminate either imprisonment or fine altogether. The proviso does not make the sentence disjunctive. If such an interpretation is placed on these provisions then it will induce disharmony in the provisions of section 16, which the legislature even remotely did not seem to intend.

(3) *Court's power to lessen and enhance sentence:* The Prevention of Food Adulteration Act provides that when the conviction is under section 16(1)(a)(i) for selling an adulterated article coming within the definition of the section 2(i)(1), the Magistrate by recording adequate and special reasons has jurisdiction to award a sentence less than the minimum. In an appeal under section 377 of the Criminal Procedure Code the High Court may interfere with the sentence if no reasons for awarding a lesser sentence are recorded by the Magistrate. Again, if the reasons recorded by the Magistrate are irrelevant, extraneous, without materials and grossly inadequate, the High Court will be justified in enhancing the sentence.

(4) If a case is covered by the various clauses of the proviso, the court has a discretion to impose a lesser punishment than the minimum prescribed. Likewise, if the case is not covered by the proviso, then no option is left to the court to impose a sentence lower than the minimum prescribed.

(5) Simply because the proviso to section 16(1) is applicable in a case, it does not follow that a court would be justified in awarding punishment which is less than the minimum prescribed in the section unless there are adequate and special reasons which have to be recorded in the judgment. That besan was sold in the same condition in which it was bought is no special reason.

OBJECT OF SEVERE PUNISHMENT UNDER THE ACT

(1) The object of providing a minimum substantive sentence and substantial pecuniary punishment is to discourage and deter anti-social elements in the society who motivated by avarice cause incalculable harm to human health. The severe punishment the legislature prescribed is an expression of righteous indication of the community against the offences of this kind with the object of preserving and promoting the well-being of human society. It is, therefore, clear that a relaxation from the rigour of the minimum is permitted only for special reasons to be mentioned in the judgment. Such reasons are required to be adequate and sufficiently weighty. The court has to further express these reasons in the judgment enabling the superior courts and the society to know the grounds for the grant of indulgence. The court while awarding punishment has to seriously consider the command of the law and the ambit of the judicial discretion conferred by it.

(2) In view of the widespread evil of adulteration and in order to eradicate the evil to an appreciable extent, a deterrent sentence is the only way. Mere imposition of fine is preposterous inasmuch as the offender can easily afford to part with a share of a gains made out of such malpractice for days together. It is only a sentence of imprisonment that can deter such persons and make them think twice before indulging in such antisocial malpractices. In view of all-out efforts that is presently being made to put down all antisocial and economic offences it is the imperative duty of the courts also to do their utmost to help in the eradication of such an evil which is widely prevalent in the society and has at present reached its climax. So despite the fact that the accused was 60 years old a sentence of rigorous imprisonment cannot be dispensed with.

(3) The crime of adulteration is not against an individual who suffers on account of drinking adulterated milk, testing

it to be pure and genuine, but against the society at large and the adulterator is therefore an offender who is committing this heinous crime day in and day out against all. This crime is very seldom detected, because it is practiced unnoticed and a large majority of such adulterators remains undetected. If the courts show unwarranted and wholly misplaced mercy for giving any benefit to these culprits who commit the crime ruthlessly by repeating it, courts are guilty of indiscrete and unintended abetment of such social crime.

(4) To allow the accused to get away by paying a naively negligible fine of one hundred rupees is to ignore the gravity of food offences. In a country when consumerism as a movement has not developed, the common man is at the mercy of the vicious dealer. And when the primary necessaries of life are sold with spurious admixtures for making profit, his only protection is the Prevention of Food Adulteration Act and the court. If offenders can get away with it by payment of a trivial fine, as in the present case, it brings the law into contempt and its enforcement a mockery

(5) The courts while awarding sentence should not lose sight of the fact that adulteration in articles of food harms the health of the nation and those who indulge in adulteration in articles of food are parasites of the society and where an offence is made out against them, proper and adequate punishment, commensurate with the gravity of the offence, should normally be awarded to them. The proviso to section 16 gives power to the court to award even less than the minimum prescribed sentence, for special and adequate reasons, but its resort has to be in exceptional cases. It is neither desirable nor possible to lay down exhaustively the circumstances when the court may award less than the prescribed minimum sentence but resort to the proviso to section 16 may be had where the trial has

been very protracted; the accused is a person of old age or is otherwise ill; the offence is of a technical nature, the degree of adulteration is very negligible and the like, and then again the reasons must be apparent on the face of the order for the scrutiny of the courts of appeal and revision.

(6) Adulteration of an article of food is a serious anti-social offence which must be visited with exemplary punishment.

(7) The evil of adulteration of food has spread its net so wide that it is posing a serious threat to the health of the whole society. The parliament too has considered it fit and proper in public interest to amend the law by enhancing penalties for offences against the law of prevention of food adulteration. It is undoubtedly a matter of grave concern to the whole society and is indeed mortifying to observe that unadulterated food stuffs are so extremely difficult for the common man to obtain in the open market. The situation has assumed such a serious magnitude that offences of the type must, in the interest of the society, call for deterrent sentence.

(8) The offences under the Act are a peril to the health of citizens and as such call for deterrent punishment.

(9) Although the two main objects of punishing an offender are (i) to reform the offender and rehabilitate him as a useful member of the society and (ii) to deter other persons from committing similar offence undue leniency shown in the matter of awarding of sentence defeats both these objects. Offenders connected with adulteration of food are social offences – these, are offences against the society at large and only deterrent punishment to the offender can create a sense of fear in the minds of those who indulge in such anti-social offences. The incidents of adulteration in articles of food have become so widespread that it has assumed alarming proportion and has become a menance to the society.

(10) *Extenuating. circumstances should be recorded for awarding a lesser punishment:* The object of providing a minimum substantive sentence and substantial pecuniary punishment is to a discourage and deter antisocial elements who motivated by avarice cause incalculable harm to human health. The severe punishment that the legislature prescribed is an expression of righteous indication of the community against the offences of this kind with thee object of preserving and promoting the well-being of human society. It is, therefore clear that a relaxation from the rigour of the minimum is permitted-only for special reasons to be mentioned in the judgment. Such reasons are required to be adequate and sufficiently weighty. The court the superior courts and the society to know the grounds fort he grant of indulgence. The court while awarding punishment has to seriously consider the command of the law and the ambit of the judicial discretion conferred by it.

POWER OF COURT TO GIVE LESSER PUNISHMENT

The Prevention of Food Adulteration Act provides that when conviction is under section 16(1)(a)(i) for selling an adulterated articles coming within the definition of the section 2(i)(1), the Magistrate by recording adequate and special reason has jurisdiction to award a sentence less than the minimum. In the appeal under section 377 of the Criminal Procedure Code the High Court may interfere with the sentence if no reasons for awarding a lesser sentence are recorded by the Magistrate. Again, if the reasons recorded by the Magistrate are irrelevant, extraneous on without materials or grossly inadequate, the High Court will be justified in enhancing the sentence.

CHAPTER 19

CENTRAL COMMITTEE FOR FOOD STANDARDS

The Central Government shall, constitute a Committee called the Central Committee for Food Standards to advise the Central Government and the State Governments on matters arising out of the administration of this Act and to curry out the other functions assigned to it under this Act.

CONSTITUTION OF THE COMMITTEE
[Section 3(2)]

The committee shall consist of the following members, namely:-

(1) The Director-General, Health Services, *ex officio* who shall be the Chairperson;

(2) The Director of the Central Food Laboratory or, in a case where more than one Central Food Laboratory is established, the Directors of such Laboratories, *ex officio*;

(3) Two experts nominated by the Central Government;

(4) One representative each of the Departments of Food and Agriculture in the Central Ministry of Food and Agriculture and one representative each of the Central Ministries of Commerce, Defence, Industry and Supply and Railways, nominated by the Central Government;

(5) One representative each nominated by the Government of each State;

(6) Two representatives nominated by the Central Government to represent the union territories;

(7) One representative each, nominated by the Central Government, to represent the agricultural, commercial and industrial interests;

(8) Five representatives nominated by the Central Government, to represent the consumers interests, one of whom shall be from the hotel industry;

(9) One representative of the medical profession nominated by the Indian Council of Medical Research;

(10) One representative nominated by the Indian Standards Institution referred to in clause (e) of Section 2 of the Indian Standards Institution (Certification Marks) Act, 1952 (36 of 1952).

The members of the Committee referred to in clauses (3), (4), (5), (6), (7), (8), (9), and (10) shall, unless their seats become vacant either by resignation, death or otherwise, be entitled to hold office for three years and shall be eligible for renomination. The functions of the Committee may be exercised notwithstanding any vacancy therein.

The committee may appoint such and so many sub-committees as it deems fit and may appoint to them persons who are not members of the Committee to exercise such powers and perform such duties as may, subject to such conditions, if any, as the Committee may impose, be delegated to them by the Committee.

The Committee may, subject to the previous approval of the Central Government, make bye-laws for the purpose of regulating its own procedure and the transaction of its business.

Appointment of Secretary and other Staff

According to Section 3-A the Central Government shall appoint a Secretary to the Committee who shall, under the control and direction of the Committee, exercise such powers and perform such duties as may be prescribed or as may be delegated to him by the Committee.

CENTRAL FOOD LABORATORY

The Central Government shall establish one or more Central Food Laboratory or Laboratories to carry out the functions entrusted to the Central Food Laboratory.

The Central Government may, also specify any laboratory or institute as a Central Food Laboratory.

The Central Government may, after consultation with the Committee, make rules prescribing –

(1) The functions of a Central Food Laboratory and the local area or areas within which such functions may be carried out;

(2) The procedure for submission to the said Laboratory of samples of articles of food for analysis or tests, the forms of the Laboratory's reports thereon and the fees payable in respect of such reports;

(3) Such other matters as may be necessary or expedient to enable the said Laboratory to carry out its functions.

In addition to the functions entrusted to the Laboratory by the Act, the Laboratory shall carry out the following functions, namely:

(1) Analysis of samples of food sent by any officer or authority authorized by the Central Government for the purpose and submission of the certificate of analysis to the authorities concerned;

(2) Investigation for the purpose of fixation of standard of any article of food;

(3) Investigation, in collaboration with the laboratories of Public Analysis in the various States and such other laboratories

and institutions which the Central Government may approve in this behalf for the purpose of standardizing methods of analysis.

The laboratories shall carry out the functions entrusted to them by the Act or these rules in respect of the respective local areas as given in Table 19.1

TABLE 19.1: Name of Central Food Laboratories and their specified areas

Name of the Central Food Laboratory		Local Area
(1)		(2)
(1) The Central Food Laboratory, Mysore–570013.	:	The State of Andhra Pradesh, Karnataka, Kerala, Maharashtra and Tamil Nadu and the Union Territories of Lakshadweep and Pondicherry
(2) The Central Food Laboratory, Pune–411001	:	The State of Gujarat and Madhya Pradesh including Chhatisgarh and Union Territories of Dadra and Nagar Haveli and Goa, Daman and Diu.
(3) The Central Food Laboratory, Ghaziabad–201001	:	The States of Haryana, Himachal Pradesh, Jammu and Kashmir, Punjab, Rajasthan and Uttar Pradesh including Uttaranchal and Union Territories of Chandigarh and Delhi.
(4) The Central Food Laboratory, Kolkata–700016	:	The state of Assam, Bihar, including Jharkhand Manipur, Meghalya, Nagaland, Orissa, Tripura and West Bengal and the Union Territories of the Andaman and Nicobar Island, Arunachal Pradesh and Mizoram.

ANALYSIS OF FOOD SAMPLES

(1) Samples of food for analysis whether under sub-section (2) of Section 13 of the Act or under clause (a) of Rule

3 shall be sent either through a messenger or by registered post in a sealed packet, enclosed together with a memorandum in Form I (Ref. Fig. 19A) in an outer cover addressed to the Director.

(2) The container as well as the outer covering of the packet shall be marked with a distinguished number

(3) A copy of the memorandum and a specimen impression of the seal used to seal the container and the cover shall be sent separately by registered post to the Director.

(4) On receipt of the packet, it shall be openly either by the Director or by an officer authorized in writing in that behalf by the Director who shall record the condition of the seal on the container.

(5) After test or analysis, the certificate thereof shall be supplied forthwith to the sender in Form II.

(6) The fees payable in respect of such a certificate shall be Rs. 40 per sample of food analyzed.

(7) Certificates issued under these rules by the Laboratory shall be signed by the Director.

The Director's certificate that "the seals were intact" is enough proof that the requirements of Rule 4 has been complied with.

In the absence of any material to show that the memo and the specimen impression of the seal were actually sent to the Director by registered post, no presumption under section 114 of Evidence Act could be drawn that Rule 4(3) was followed because the true effect of section 114 of the Evidence act was that if an official act was proved to have been done, it would be presumed to have been regularly done, but it did not raise any presumption that an act was done of which there was no evidence.

A copy of memorandum and a specimen impression of the seal shall be sent separately by registered post to the Director. When neither the registration receipt nor the acknowledgment

FORM I

[See Rule 4(1)]

MEMORANDUM TO THE DIRECTOR, CENTRAL FOOD LABORATORY

From

____

____

To

The Director,
Central Food Laboratory

____

____

MEMORANDUM

No.____________________ Dated the ______________200______

1. I send herewith under the provisions of Section 13(2) of the Prevention of Food Adulteration Act, 1954, sample(s) of a food purporting to be ______________ for test or analysis and request that a report on the result of the test or analysis may be supplied to this Court:

   (1) Distinguishing No. of the containers and outer covering ....

   (2) Particulars of offence alleged ....

   (3) Matter on which opinion required ....

(2) A fee of Rs. 40 has been deposited in the Treasury creditable under the "Receipt Head-082 - Public Health, Sanitation and Water Supply-Fees and Fines etc." and treasury challan for the same is enclosed.

(3) A copy of the memorandum and the specimen impression of the seal used to seal the container and the cover are sent separately by Registered Post.

Magistrate 1st Class/
Presidency Magistrate

Figure 19A: Specimen Form I: Memorandum to the Director, Central Food Laboratory

receipt in this connection is produced before the court there cannot be any presumption of section 114 of the Evidence Act that it is done in accordance with the procedure. Proof of compliance of the procedure is essential for the success of the prosecution.

The specimen impression of the seal and a copy of the memorandum shall be sent separately by registered post to the Director of Central Food Laboratory serves a special purpose for the accused. It assumes greater significance because the fate of the accused depends upon the certificate issued by the Director (Ref Fig. 19B) which is final and conclusive evidence of the facts stated therein and which are not open to challenge by; the accused in any manner whatsoever. Not only can the accused not challenge the contents of the certificate by leading any other evidence but he cannot also challenge the contents by requiring the Director to be cross-examined by him. Once the director issues a certificate that the sample of food sent to him was adulterated, the fate of the accused is sealed. It is not open to him even to ask the court to get back the food sample analysed by the Director for further analysis by his own expert. When the final and conclusive character attributed to the certificate issued by the Director produces such a far-reaching consequence, there is no doubt that all the provisions of law which relate to it and which confer even the smallest safeguard on the accused must be construed strictly. Therefore, the provisions of Rule 4(3) in so far as they require that a specimen impression of the seal used by the court to seal the container and a cover and a copy of the memorandum shall be sent separately to the Director are mandatory.

A sample which reaches the Director of Central Food Laboratory passes through three stages. It originates in the court which sends it, it travels from the place of its origin to the place of its delivery and before it is finally delivered to the Central Food Laboratory, its journey ends at the post office which serves the Central Food Laboratory now if any mischief or interference is committed at any of these stages with the sample packet, it will be difficult for the Director to discover it because whoever

FORM II
[See Rule 4 (5)]

Certificate No.

CERTIFICATE OF TEST OR ANALYSIS BY THE CENTRAL FOOD LABORATORY

Certified that the sample(s), bearing number .... purporting to be a sample/samples of .... received on .... with Memorandum No .... dated .... from.................. was in a condition fit for analysis and has/have been tested/analysed and that the result/results of such test(s)/analysis/are stated below:

____

____

____

2. The condition of seals on the container and the outer covering on receipt was as follows:

____

____

____

Director
Central Food Laboratory

Place:

Date:

Figure 19B: Specimen Form II: Certificate of Test or Analysis by the CFL

interferes with the seal on the container will also be able to interfere with the specimen impression of the seal enclosed therewith, because both are available to him at one and the same time and they can safely be tempered with. It may happen at the place where it originates or in the course of its journey or at the post office where its journey ends. If the seal which the container bears and the specimen impression of the seal are found in one and the same packet, then any one who interferes with it will be able to successfully achieve his object, because he will be able to interfere with both, since both are available to him in one and the same time. That will not be the situation if the specimen impression of the seal is sent separately either through a messenger or by registered post to the Directory of Central Food Laboratory, because whoever interferes with the seal on the container will have the specimen impression of the seal available to him for being interfered with, since it must have been sent separately either through a messenger or by registered post. Needless to say that whoever thinks of interfering with the seal on the container will also be able to successfully interfere with the seal on the outer cover. As a result, the important and valuable safeguard which has been conferred upon the accused will be lost will become illusory if the seal on the container and the specimen impression of the seal, both being as a label at one and the same time, have been interfered with by some unscrupulous mischief-monger, because the Director who is not available to the accused for cross-examination will not be able to know in such a situation whether the seal on the container has been interfered with or not.

Since the requirement of section 13(2) is mandatory, the statutory safeguard provided by Rule 4 must be interpreted in a manner consistent with the mandatory requirement. The scheme of Rule 4(3) is that the court will have to send along with a copy of the memorandum a specimen impression of the seal used by the court to seal the container and outer cover. The procedure required under Rule 4(3) is mandatory.

In view of the mandatory provisions of Rule 4(3) and section 13(2) it is clear that the court's seal has to be applied both to the container and the paper cover and it is the specimen impression of the court's seal which has to be sent separately by registered post to the Director, Central Food Laboratory along with a copy of the memorandum under Rule 4(3). That is why even the memorandum in Form I provides that a copy thereof and a specimen impression of the seal upon on the container and the cover shall be sent by the court separately by registered post. That seal is clearly court's seal within the meaning of Rule 4(3) and section 13(2).

The provision of Rule 4(3) are held to be mandatory. Unless the above mandatory provisions of the Rule are complied with, the report of the Directors of the Central Food Laboratory cannot be treated as evidence and much less as final and conclusive evidence of the facts stated therein as contemplated by sub-section (5) of section 13 of the act.

Under rule 7(3) of the 1955, it is obligatory upon the Public Analyst that after the analysis has been completed he has forthwith to issue the certificate incorporating the result of the analysis.

Similarly, it is laid down in Rule 4(5) of the Rules that after the test for analysis, the certificate has to be supplied forthwith to the authority sending the sample for analysis. These two Rules provide for imperative obligation upon the Public Analyst to issue the certificate immediately after the sample of article of food sent to him has been analysed.

The word "shall." used in Rule 4(5) and 7(3) in a directory or permissive sense. It means no more than what is conveyed by the word 'may'. If the word 'shall forthwith' are construed in mandatory and restricted sense, they will not only impede and tend to defeat the object and aim of the Act and the rules but also make them unworkable.

The main purpose of the Act and the Rules make thereunder are to ensure purity of food and the maintenance of public health by eradicating the evils of adulteration of food. These objects are likely to be frustrated if the words "shall forthwith" in the aforesaid Rules are ascribed a narrow mandatory connotation because the slightest delay on the part of the Public Analyst in analyzing or sending the report would vitiate the trial enabling many a person guilty of the social escape from the hands of law.

The Public Analyst and the Director are supposed to deal with numerous cases received by them from various places. To expect them to analyse, compile the data and send the result, the moment they receive the samples, would be enjoying on them to perform magic tricks divorced from the realities of the work-a-day world. It is wondered if their laboratories are equipped with electronic computers.

CHAPTER 20

STANDARDS OF QUALITY OF FOOD

STANDARDS OF QUALITY OF THE VARIOUS ARTICLES OF FOOD

The standards of quality of the various articles of food specified in Appendix B to the Prevention of Food Adulteration Rules have been prescribed by the Central Government on the advice of a committee which included in its composition persons considered experts in the field of food technology and food analysis. In the circumstances, if a rule has to be struck down as imposing unreasonable or discriminatory standards, it could not be done merely on *a priori* reasoning but only as a scientific analysis. Simply because the accused pleaded that the standards prescribed are too high, the court cannot consider it unreasonable on unconstitutional. The test of Reichert or Reichert-Meissal value of *ghee* is one of the important tests for detecting adulteration with certain vegetable oils by determining the proportion of the volatile soluble acids in *ghee*. The presence of the adulterant disturbs the ratio existing in acids and volatile and non-volatile acids. The Reichert value of pure *ghee* is not constant but is dependent on several factors among them the breed of the cattle to be found in an area, whether the cattle are pasture fed or stall fed, and the nature of the additional feed given, the nature of terrain, the rainfall and climatic condition etc. The feed available for the cattle is a very material and determining factor. In the absence of any pleading or proof the court was not justified in holding that the basis on which the Reichert value had been prescribed for the several areas in the country was not based on any rational classification and in holding that it was sufficient if any vendor of ghee in the country satisfied the minimum standard prescribed for any area under these rules.

In his report the Public Analyst described the sample to be not of standard purity without giving any details thereof. Non-disclosure of details amounted to a mere formal defect and it did not vitiate the prosecution.

SALE OF BUTTER MILK

No standard for its content prescribed. A person selling butter milk cannot be convicted under Sections 7 and 16(1)(a)(i).

In the case of adulterated mustard oil, even if the test for argemone oil was not applied, once it is found that the specific value and the Bellier's test show that the sample was not in conformity with the statutory requirements, the opinion of the Analyst that the oil was adulterated must be accepted. Non-conformity with the requirements in respect of any of the tests laid down in Item A.17.06 of Appendix B to the Rules is itself sufficient to show that the oil is not of the standard of purity required by the statute.

The Food Inspector who takes a sample of food for analyses is authorized to give a notice in writing of his intention to do so to the person from whom sample is taken. He can take any article of food which he suspects to be adulterated or which he suspects would not conform to the standard laid down in the Rules. The "note" appended is neither illegal nor does it travel beyond the scope of section 5 of the Act. Therefore, if the Food Inspector demands any of the various types of milk and if there is no indication on the type of milk. Then under the "note" referred to above which is nothing more or less than a rule itself indicates that the standard to be applied for analysis of such milk will be that which has been prescribed for buffalo milk.

MUSTARD OIL CONTAINING SOME TIL OIL - EFFECT OF

The standard of mustard oil prescribed in Item A.17.06 provides for a negative test for argemones oil and not for til or any other edible oil. Similarly, the standard of mustard oil seed prescribed in Item A.05.15 permits presence of any other oil seed up to 7 per cent but not of *Argemone maxicana* Linn. Where in the sample all the ingredients of mustard oil were found to be within the limit prescribed in Item A.17.06, it was held that the sample of mustard oil simply because it contained some til oil (not exceeding 7 per cent) could not be said to be adulterated.

SEA CUSTOM LAWS AND POWERS OF CUSTOMS OFFICERS

The law for the time being in force relating see customs and to goods, the impart of which is prohibited by section 18 of the Sea Customs Act, 1878 (8 of 1878) shall, subject to the provisions of section 16 of this Act, apply in respect of articles of food, the import of which is prohibited under section 5 of this Act, and officers of Customs and officers empowered under that Act to perform the duties imposed thereby on a Customs Collector and other officers of Customs shall have the same powers in respect of such articles of food as they have for the time being in respect of such goods as aforesaid.

Without prejudice to the provisions of sub-section (1) the Customs Collector, or any officer of the Government authorized by the Central Government in this behalf, may detain any imported package which he suspects to contain any article of food the import of which is prohibited under section 5 of this Act and shall forthwith report such detention to the Director of the Central Food Laboratory and, if required by him, forward the package or send samples of any suspected article of food found therein to the said Laboratory.

PROHIBITION OF MANUFACTURE, SALE, ETC. OF CERTAIN ARTICLES OF FOOD

No person shall himself or by any person on his behalf manufacture for sale, or store, sell or distribute –

(1) Any adulterated food;

(2) Any misbranded food;

(3) Any article of food for the sale of which a licence is prescribed, except in accordance with the condition of the licence;

(4) Any article of food for sale of which is for the time being prohibited by the Food (Health) Authority in the interest of public health;

(5) Any article of food in contravention of any other provision of this Act or of any rule made thereunder; of

(6) Any adulterant.

A person shall be deemed to store any adulterated food or misbranded food or any article of food referred to in clause (iii) or (iv) or clause (v) if he stores such food for the manufacture therefrom of any article of food for sale.

Import of certain articles of food is prohibited under Section 5:

(1) Any adulterated food;

(2) Any misbranded food;

(3) Any article of food for the import of which a licence is prescribed, except in accordance with the conditions of the licence; and

(4) Any article of food in contravention of any other provision of this Act or of any rule made thereunder.

CHAPTER 21

ANALYSIS OF FOOD: Public Analyst and Food Inspectors

The Central Government or the State Government may, by notification in the Official Gazette, appoint such persons as it thinks fit, having the prescribed qualifications to be public analysts for such local areas as may be assigned to them by the Central Government or the State Government, as the case may be.

No person who has any financial interest in the manufacture, import or sale of any article of food shall be appointed to be a public analyst under this section.

Different public analysts may be appointed for different articles of food.

PUBLIC ANALYST

Qualifications of Public Analyst

A person shall not be qualified for appointment as a public analyst, unless he-

(i) Is a graduate in science, with chemistry as one of the subjects from a University established in India by law or has equivalent qualifications recognized by the Central Government in this behalf and has not less than seven years' experience in the analysis of food in any, of the laboratories recognized and notified by Government of

India and included in the list issued by that Government for such purposes; or

(ii) Is an M.Sc. in Chemistry or Biochemistry or Agricultural Chemistry or Food technology or Foods and Drugs from a University established in India by law or possesses qualifications of Associateship of the Institution of Chemists (India) by examination in the section of analysis of food conducted by the Institution of Chemists (India) or has equivalent qualifications recognized by the Central Government in this behalf, and has not less than three years' experience in the analysis of food in any of the laboratories referred to in analysis (i); or

(iii) Is a graduate in medicine from a University established in India by law or has equivalent qualifications recognized by the Central Government in this behalf, with post-graduate qualification in Public Health or Biochemistry and has not less than three years' experience in the analysis of food in any of the laboratories referred to in clause (i); or

(iv) Is a Fellow of the Royal Institute of Chemistry of Great Britain (Branch E) with at least one year's experience of food analysis in India:

A person who is a public analyst on the date of amendment of the Prevention of Food Adulteration (Amendment) Rules, 1968 may continue to hold office as such, subject to the terms and conditions of service applicable to him, even though he does not fulfil the qualification laid down in clauses (i) to (iv).

Duties of Public Analyst

On receipt of a package containing a sample for analyst from Food Inspector or any other person the Public Analyst or an officer authorized by him shall compare the seals on the container and the outer cover with specimen impression received separately and shall note the condition of the seals thereon.

The public analyst shall cause to be analyzed such samples of article of food as may be sent to him by food inspector or by any other person under the Act.

The public analyst shall, within a period of 45 days from the date of receipt of any sample for analysis, deliver to the Local (Health) Authority a report of the result of such analysis in Form III (Ref Fig. 21A).

Where any such sample does not conform to the provision of the Act or these rules, the public analyst shall deliver four copies of such report to the said Authority:

Provided further that the public analyst shall forward a copy of such report also to the person who purchased an article of food and forwarded the same to him for analysis under Section 12 of the Act.

Who can Purchase Sample for Analysis?

If the appointment of a Sanitary Inspector as a Food Inspector is not valid, he cannot be a purchaser within the meaning of section 12, as the section specifically excludes him from the category of purchasers.

What Happens if Payment is not Made for Purchase Such Sample?

Purchaser or article of food, purporting to act as the Food Inspector, sending article for analysis to the Government Public Analyst without payment of fees. If the state government does not care to recover the prescribed fees from him and if the Public Analyst sends report of analysis without payment of any fees that would not make report inadmissible in evidence or otherwise vitiate the proceedings.

The provisions of Section 12 apply when a person sending sample is not a Food Inspector - sample so sent must be deemed to be the sample submitted under the Act and the report of the Public Analyst is admissible in evidence.

FORM III
[See Rue 7(3)]
REPORT BY THE PUBLIC ANALYST

Report No.................

I hereby certify that I, ... Public Analyst for .... duly appointed under provision of the Prevention of Food Adulteration Act, 1954, received on the .... day of .... 200 .... from .... a sample of .... for analysis, properly sealed and fastened, and that I found that seal intact and unbroken.

The seal fixed on the container and the outer cover of the sample tallied with the specimen impression of the seal separately sent by the food inspector and the sample was in a condition fit for analysis.

I further certify that I have/had caused to be analysed the aforementioned sample, and declare the result of the analysis to be as follows:

____

____

and am of the opinion that __________________

____

____

Signed this ...... day of .... , 200.....

(Signature)
Public Analyst

Address ....
....

Figure 21A: Specimen Form III: Report of the Public Analyst

A Private Person also can Send Sample for Analysis by the Public Analyst

Though Section 12 speaks of purchaser sending article for analysis by the Public Analyst the relevant rules made under the Act enable any persons to do the same on payment of fees. Hence section 12 is not violative of Article 14 of the Constitution.

A member of the public can also purchase article of food for analysis under this section.

Even if the appointment of Food Inspector is invalid he can act as private purchaser and submit article of food for analysis to the Public Analyst under this section.

REPORT OF PUBLIC ANALYST

(1) The public analyst shall deliver, in such form as may be prescribed (Ref Fig. 20A) a report to the Local (Health) Authority of the result of the analysis of any article of food submitted to him for analysis.

(2) On receipt of the report of the result of the analysis under sub-section (1) to the effect that the article of food is adulterated, the

Local (Health) Authority shall, after the institution of prosecution against the person from whom the sample of the article of food was taken and the persons, if any, whose name, address and other particulars have been disclosed under section 14-A, forward, in such manner as may be prescribed, a copy of the report of the result of the analysis to such person or persons, as the case may be, informing such person or persons that it is so desired, either or both of them may make an application to the court within a period of ten days from the date of receipt of the copy of the report to get the sample of the article of food kept by the Local (Health) Authority analysed by the Central Food Laboratory.

When an application is made to the court under subsection (2), the court shall require the Local (Health) Authority to forward the part or parts of the sample kept by the said Authority and upon such requisition being made, and said Authority shall forward the part or parts of the sample to the court within a period of five days from the date of receipt of such requisition.

On receipt of the part or parts of the sample from the Local (Health) Authority under sub-section (2-A), the court shall first ascertain that the mark and seal or fastening as provided in clause (b) of sub-section (1) of section 11 are intact and the signature or thumb-impression, s the case may be, is not tampered with, and dispatch the part or, as the case may be, one of the parts of the sample under its own seal to the Director of the Central Food Laboratory who shall thereupon send a certificate to the court in the prescribed form within one month from the date of receipt of the part of the sample specifying the result of the analysis.

Where two parts of the sample have been sent to the court and only one part of the sample has been sent by the court to the Director of the Central Food Laboratory under sub-section (2-B), the court shall, as soon as practicable, return the remaining part to the Local (Health) Authority and that Authority shall destroy that part after the certificate from the Director of the Central Food Laboratory has been received by the court.

Where the part of the sample sent by the court to the Director of the Central Food Laboratory is lost or damaged, the court shall require the Local (Health) Authority to forward the part of the sample, if any, retained by it to the court and on receipt thereof, the court shall in the manner provided in sub-section.

Until the receipt of the certificate of the result of the analysis from the Director of the Central Food Laboratory, the court shall not continue with the proceedings pending before it in relation to the prosecution.

If, after considering the report, if any, of the Food Inspector or otherwise, the Local (Health) Authority is of the opinion that the report delivered by the Public Analyst under sub-section (1) is erroneous, the said Authority shall forward one of the parts of the sample kept by it to any other public analyst for analysis and if the report of the result of the analysis of that part of the sample by that other public analyst is to the effect that the article of food is adulterated, the provisions of sub-section (2) to (2-D) shall, so far as may be, apply.

The certificate issued by the Director of the Central Food Laboratory under sub-section (2B) shall supersede the report given by the Public Analyst under sub-section (1).

Where a certificate obtained from the Director of the Central Food Laboratory under sub-section (2B) is produced in any proceeding under this Act, or under sections 272 to 276 of the Indian Penal Code (45 of 1860), it shall not be necessary in such proceeding to produce any part of the sample of taken for analysis.

Any document purporting to be a report signed by a public analyst, unless it has been superseded under sub-section (3), or any document purporting to be a certificate signed by the Director of the Central Food Laboratory, may be used as evidence of facts stated therein in any proceeding under this Act or under section 272 to 276 of the Indian Penal Code (45 of 1960).

Any document purporting to be a certificate signed by the Director of the Central Food Laboratory not being a certificate with respect of the part of the sample of any article of food referred to in the proviso to sub-section (1-A) of Section 16 shall be final and conclusive evidence of the facts stated therein.

In this section and in clause (f) of sub-section (1) of section 16."Director of the Central Food Laboratory" shall include the officer for the time being in charge of any Food Laboratory (by whatever designation he is known) recognized by the Central Government for the purposes of this section.

DUTIES OF PUBLIC ANALYST

Where law has prescribed in case of milk a minimum content of non-fat solids all lumped together, it is not necessary for the

Public Analyst to give quantitative break up of different kinds of non-fat solids in his report.

The public analyst need not state how calculation were made in arising at the result. He need not himself take analysis, it is quite sufficient it to get it done under his supervision. The report of the public analyst need not contain mode or particulars of analysis nor the test applied - but should contain the results of the analysis namely data from which it can be inferred whether article of good was or not adulterated. The time limit is not fixed by the act but the examination by the public analyst showed not be unreasonably delayed. He showed return the container with his report - this will eliminate any doubt as to the wrong sample being reported on.

The public analyst should not in his report state e.g., milk sample contained quantity of added water. His duty is to state the result of his analysis and show how much water is contained in the sample.

He is not required to compare the seal on the container with the specimen seal. The report of the Public Analyst should mention the time and date of examination of article.

The accused has right to call the Public Analyst to be examined and cross-examined under Section 257 Criminal Procedure Code. The fact that the certificate of the Director of the Control Food Laboratory supersedes the report of the Public Analyst and is conclusive and final does not limit this right of the accused. In view of specific rule of evidence in Section 13(5), it is necessary that the Public Analyst should be examined as witness. As regards failure to examine the Public Analyst as a witness in the case no blame can be laid on the prosecution. The report of the Public Analyst was there and if either the court or the accused wanted him to be examined as a witness, the appropriate steps would have been taken. The prosecution cannot fail solely on the ground that the Public Analyst had not been called in the case.

The act of causing the sample to be analysed is one of the duties of the Public Analyst. It cannot, therefore, be contended with any show of reason that the rule making authority exceeded its powers under section 23(1)(e) in providing that the act of causing the sample of food to be analysed will be one of the duties of the Public Analyst.

In fact when the rules allow the Public Analysis to get the analysis done by some one subordinate to him under his own supervision, he cannot certify that it was the result of his analysis. The difference between the prescribed form and the form in which the certificate was given was that instead of the words "my analysis" the words "the analysis" had been used.

There is no difference whether the words "the analysis" were used or "my analysis" were used. The report that the Analyst had submitted described in a more accurate manner whatever he was actually expected to do and what in fact he did, though there was a deviation from the form. In any case even if the report was not on the prescribed form, under section 13(5) of the Act it was a document purporting to be a report signed by a Public Analyst and was evidence of the fact stated therein.

REPORT OF PUBLIC ANALYST – ADMISSIBILITY

(1) It is a settled law that the report of the Public Analyst is admissible in evidence without any other proof. The presumption under Section 114 Illus. (e) of the Indian Evidence Act would apply to the case and it has to be presumed that the Public Analyst acted in accordance with the Rules, though the presumption is a rebuttable one.

(2) Under Rule 7(1) of Rules, 1955 the public Analyst or officer authorized by him has to compare seal on container and outer cover of sample with specimen impression received separately and to note condition of seals thereon. When the Analyst states in report that seals of sample

were found intact it is presumed that he compared those seals with specimen impression.

When the Public Analyst did not mention in his report that he had actually compared the seals on packet with the specimen impression which had been sent to him it. The report of the Public Analyst in Form III need not specify that he had compared the seal on the packed with the specimen seal sent separately. There is no infirmity in not mentioning it.

The act of causing the sample to be analysed is one of the duties of the Public Analyst. It cannot, therefore, be contended with any show of reasons that the rule-making authority exceeded its powers under Section 23(1)(e) in providing that the act of causing the sample of food to be analysed will be one of the duties of the Public Analyst.

The Public Analyst has to compare a seal on the container and the outer cover with the specimen impression received separately on receipt of the packet containing sample for analysis.

There was absence of a statement in the report that before analysis the seals were compared and found identical. Non-mention of the statement did not vitiate the report.

Analysis of sample of food caused to be made by the Public Analyst and certified by him as correct is a valid report.

Specimen impression of seal is not sent to the Analyst. There is nothing with which the Public Analyst could perform his duty of comparing seal of packet of black pepper forwarded to him for analysis. It is a case of total non-compliance with rules 7(1) and 18 and as such fatal to prosecution.

The Chemist, an officer appointed by Municipal Commissioner and in service and pay of Municipal Corporation and duly authorized by the Public Analyst can validly receive sample and the memorandum impression of seal and compare the seals and make analysis of sample under the supervision of the Public Analyst.

Milk should be Stirred by the Public Analyst Before Analysis

As will appear from the instructions given to the Public Analyst, even during analysis they are advised to thoroughly shake the sample of milk because the milk fat generally accumulates at the top and if only the top portion of the sample is analysed, it will show a very high percentage of milk fat and a corresponding low percentage of non-fatty solids.

Weighment of Sample

When the accused demanded that the sample of food taken by the Food Inspector is to be weighted and when that request was made after eight months of filing of the complaint, there was inordinate delay and the trying court is justified to refuse to accept the request.

Delay in Compiling Report – Necessity of Examining the Public Analyst

The rules do not contain any direction to the Public Analyst to analyse a sample within a particular period, but the presumption is that in view of the fact that the samples that are sent to him are of a perishable nature, the analysis would be normally conducted as expeditiously as possible. The idea of adding preservative is not to prolong the life of the samples indefinitely but to keep it in its original state for a limited period. It would, therefore, be presumed that the analysis had been conducted soon after the sample was received. The delay in compiling the report does not necessarily mean that the analysis was also delayed. If the trying Magistrate has any doubt in regard to this aspect of the matter, he can examine the Public Analyst or get a clarification from him.

The Public Analyst has to compare the seal on the container and the outer cover with the specimen impression received separately on receipt of the packet containing sample of the food for analysis. The accused contended that the Public Analyst did not mention in the report that he had compared the specimen impression of the seal with the one on the memorandum. The presumption is that the Public Analyst must have compared the specimen impression with that of the container.

Non-compliance affects the evidentiary value of the report of the Public Analyst and conviction solely based upon it cannot be sustained.

The provisions of Rules 7 and 18 of the Rules are mandatory. Where the prosecution does not prove compliance with the provisions of rules by leading necessary evidence, it will deprive the report of the Public Analyst of its evidentiary value and will make it impossible for the court to base a conviction solely upon such report.

Rules 7 and 18 are intended to prevent the possibility of tampering with the sample before it reaches the Public Analyst. When the report of the Public Analyst mentions that the seal fixed on the container of the sample tallied with the specimen impression of the seal separately sent by the Food Inspector and the same was in a condition fit for analysis, this could conclusively establish that the seals fixed on the container of the seals were separately sent by the Food Inspector. There was therefore full compliance with Rules 7 and 18.

The expression "shall" has no doubt been used in both Rules 7 and 18, but that by itself cannot be a true guide to the exact nature of the rules as to whether they are mandatory or directory. It is, however, one of the cardinal principles of interpretation of statutes that when the statute requires that something shall be done in a particular manner or form without expressly declaring what shall be the consequence of non-compliance, the duty of the court is to get at the legislature and in doing so one must look to the subject matter and consider the relation of the provision to the general object intended to be secured by the Act and upon a review of the case in that aspect decide whether the matter is called imperative or only directory. Having regard to the intention of the legislature as evidenced by the various provisions of the Act and the Rules, Rules 7 and 18 prescribing duties by the

Public Analyst after receipt of the package containing sample for analysis are mandatory in nature.

A duty is cast upon the Public Analyst to compare the seal on the container and the outer cover with the specimen impression of the seal received separately and to note the condition of the seals thereon. The report of the Public Analyst being of the vital importance there is all the more the importance of checks and safeguards and as such Rules 7 and 18 are mandatory in nature.

When the record does not establish that the Food Inspector failed to send a specimen impression of his seal while sending the sample to the Public Analyst and that the latter failed to compare the seals, the presumption under Section 114, Illus. (e) of the Evidence Act will arise and it is not rebutted.

Report of the Public Analyst is proof of compliance of the provisions of Rules (7)(1) and 18 in absence of contrary evidence-Prosecution may lead positive evidence that the conditions prescribed in Rules 7(1) and 18 were fulfilled. If, however, there is dearth of such evidence for the prosecution, in the absence of contrary evidence, the report of the Public Analyst would be proof of the compliance of provisions of Rules 7(1) and 18.

The presumption under section 114 of the Evidence Act is that official duties are performed regularly. It has not been shown effectively as to how prejudice has been caused to the accused by the prosecution not producing or proving the office copy of the memorandum under which the sample was sent to the Public Analyst. The whole object behind sending a separate copy of the memorandum with the specimen impression of the seal is for proper identification of the sample. There has been compliance with Rule 7(1) and no prejudice has been caused for non-production that of office copy of the memorandum under which the sample was sent to the Public Analyst.

There is no direction in the Prevention of Food Adulteration Rules laying down that a report of shall not be admissible in evidence without due compliance with certain rules. It is possible evidence without due compliance with certain rules. It is possible to take the Public Analyst's report into consideration even in a case where there was non-compliance with some of the rules. Hence even if a particular rule was not followed that would not be sufficient for interfering with the conviction of the accused.

Neither Rule 7 nor Form III nor Section 13 requires the Public Analyst to state the method adopted in the technical processes involved in carrying on the analysis. If the legislature had in mind that the report of the Public Analyst could be acted upon only if further particulars necessary for enabling the court to check up the correctness of the result declared in the report also were furnished, it would have been specifically stated so in the Rules or the Act. It is not open to the court to decline to act on the strength of the result declared by the Analyst because the report is bereft of other particulars.

In order that à report of the Public Analyst may be admissible in evidence without examining the Public Analyst, it must comply strictly with the requirements of Form II which inter alia furnishes evidence of the Public Analyst having discharged his duty under Rule 7(1) as regards the identity of sample examined by him. A report of the Public Analyst as required by law is not admissible in evidence as evidence of the facts stated therein without examining the Public Analyst.

Specimen impression of seal used to seal the sample was affixed on Form VII sent along with the sample of chillies powder. The Public Analyst in his report mentioned that he found the seal "in tact" and unbroken, it was held that no objection could be taken that there was nothing in the report to show that the seal on bottle containing sample tallied with the specimen seal impression. Obviously, the report meant that the seal tallied with the specimen signature. [Rule 7 and 18 and Form VII].

If the report of the Public Analyst gave the full factual date and no opinion. The conviction can be based upon it. In such a case the Public Analyst need not he examined, but the records must show that Rules 7 and 18 are duly complied with.

Though it would be better for the Public Analyst to note the condition of the seal in the certificate in his own handwriting to show that he was satisfied as to the condition of the seal after comparison of the specimen seal sent to him separately, the contents of the printed Form III which has been prescribed under Rule 7(3) seem to satisfy the requirement of both sub-rule (1) and (3) of Rule 7.

In the report of the Public Analyst the words "my analysis" were replaced by "the analysis". This change was evidently done because the analysis was performed not by the Public Analyst himself but by a person under his supervision. There was no different whether the words "the analysis" were used or "my analysis" were used. The report that the Analyst had submitted described in a more accurate manner what he was actually expected to do and what in fact he did, though there was a deviation from the form. In any case, even if the report was not on the prescribed form, under section 13(5) of the Act it was a document purporting to be a report signed by the Public Analyst and was evidence of the facts stated therein.

Rules requiring the Food Inspector to send a copy of memorandum and specimen impression of seal used to seal the packet to the Public Analyst separately by post, such Rules being mandatory, non-compliance with Rules affects evidentiary value of the certificate of the Public Analyst and in the absence of extraneous evidence conviction based on such report is vitiated.

The Public Analyst is to send two copies of his report. The Public Analyst is to certify that the container and outer cover were properly sealed and fastened. Because of amendment made in Form III with effect from 8th July 1968 the Public Analyst is now under an additional obligation to state that the seal on the container of the sample tallies with the specimen impression on the seal separately sent by the Food Inspector and also that the sample was in a fit condition for analysis.

Rule 7(2) recognizes the fact that the Public Analyst need not examine it himself but he can have it examined and analysed by any other person under the Act. One to analyse all the articles that would be sent to him for analysis. He needs to have assistance. It is obviously for this reason that provision is made in Rule 7(2) of the Act to cause the samples to be analysed by any other person under the Act. That is also clear from Form III which uses the words: "I have caused to be analysed". This Form III is under Rule 7(3) of the Rules.

REPORT OF THE PUBLIC ANALYST – ADMISSIBILITY IN EVIDENCE

Statement in report that the sample was kept in refrigerator before analysis-statement forms part of report. Such report is admissible in evidence without production of the Public Analyst as witness. Court has, however, the power to call the Public Analyst to the court.

Rule 7(3) of the Rules does not require the Public Analyst to state in the form prescribed that the carried out the analysis in the manner mentioned in the form. It is not necessary to mention all the details of the manner in which the Public Analyst carried out the analysis. What is required of him by the form is a certificate that he has analysed the sample sent to him and on his so certifying it must be presumed that all the steps mentioned in clause (a) to (f) of item A.14 of the Appendix B of the Rules must have been followed by him.

The statement made by the Public Analyst in the report that the sample was kept in refrigerator before analysis is a part of the report and is admissible in evidence without production of the Public Analyst as a witness.

Report of the Public Analyst is dated more than a month after receipt of the sample – effect. In a case where the date of analysis is not mentioned in the report and the report is dated more than a month after the date of the receipt of the sample, the presumption would arise that the analysis was not done immediately on receipt of the sample, but much later. It is for the prosecution to rebut that presumption by examining the Public Analyst, otherwise the report cannot be admitted in evidence.

A Public Analyst analyzing a sample on 2nd and signing in the report on 9th is certainly guilty of slackness, the court however cannot throw out the prosecution on that court for not strictly complying with the provisions of Rule 7(3). In the absence of prejudice to the accused such non-compliance would not prove fatal to the prosecution. Rule 7(3) cannot thus be held to be mandatory.

Sub-rule (3) of Rule 7 of the Prevention of Food Adulteration Rules, 1955 can be meant as laying down that a prosecution can be launched at least beyond the period of 60 days (with effect from 4 January 1974 the period is reduced to 45 days) without any further unexplained delay. In normal circumstances a period of 4 months can easily be taken before the accused has any opportunity of exercising his right under section 13(2) of the Prevention of Food Adulteration Act. Where the question of delay is raised in defence the real test is whether at the time when the accused has an opportunity of exercising his right under section 13(2), the sample remains in a condition fit for analysis by the Director. Though therefore promptness in prosecuting the accused is always necessary and expedient, mere delay will not be fatal to the prosecution, unless it is established that the delay which is attributable to the prosecution has resulted in a denial or frustration of the right of the accused under section 13(2) on account of the sample having become deteriorated and unfit for analysis. It cannot be contended that the accused is not expected to retain the sample for an indefinite period, because the third sample required to be retained by the Food Inspector would always be available. In normal circumstances therefore a period of three or four months in prosecuting the accused is not fatal, subject to the condition that the provision of Rule 20 in the matter of addition of the preservative is substantially complied with.

In that case the Food Inspector filed the complaint after two and half months and it was said that he did not add requisite quantity of the formalin. It was held that the delay of two and half months in launching the prosecution was not much; and slight deviation in adding the required quantity of formalin was inconsequential. It was also pointed out that it is of utmost importance that the prosecution agency should take immediate steps to prosecute the accused soon after the report is received from the Public Analyst.

The Form of Report presented under Rule 7(3), namely Form III, is not in contravention of Form VI prescribed under Rule 12 and is not liable to be declared *ultra vires* under section 11(1)(a). Under Rule 7(3) there is an option to the Public Analyst either to analyse the sample himself or cause it to be analysed by some other competent persons. There is no real inconsistency between Form III as amended in 1960 and Form VI framed under Rule 12 in as much as the analysis done by a qualified assistant to the Public Analyst under the later's supervision would be deemed to be an analysis by the Public Analyst himself.

Rule 7(3) and Form III does not prescribe anything calling on the Public Analyst to make an endorsement to the effect that he compared the seals on the container with specimen seal sent to him.

In the case of analysis of milk the court has to be satisfied that the Public Analyst has conducted the analysis without any avoidable delay. It may be that refrigeration is added to the sample. But even in such cases the delay in conducting the analysis has to be taken into account by the court in assessing the value of the report of the Analyst. Further, in view of Rule 7 (3) in a case where the date of analysis is not mentioned in the report and the report is dated more than a month after the date of receipt of the sample, the presumption would arise that the analysis was not done immediately on receipt of the sample, but much later. It is for the prosecution, therefore, to rebut that presumption by examining the Public Analyst. Otherwise, the report will not accepted as showing the content of fat and non-fat solids at the time of taking the sample.

A sample of milk was taken from the accused on 12 September 1968 and preservative was added in requisite quantity. The sample was analysed by the Public Analyst on 16 October 1968. The prosecution was launched on 24th June 1969. There was no explanation from the prosecution for the undue delay of 8 months. Held that a sample of milk even after adding preservative can remain fit for analysis at the most for a period of 6 months, if kept under refrigeration in our country and as such the accused was deprived of his right under section 13(2) of the act.

FOOD INSPECTORS

The Central Government or the State Government may, appoint such persons as it thinks fit, having the prescribed qualifications to be food inspectors for such local areas as may be assigned to them by the Central government or the State Government, as the case may be:

Provided that no person who has nay financial interest in the manufacturer, import or sale of any article of food shall be appointed to be a food inspector under this section.

Every food inspector shall be deemed to be a public servant within the meaning of section 21 of the Indian Penal Code (45 of 1860) and shall be officially subordinate to such authority as the Government appointing him, may specify in this behalf.

Qualifications of a Food Inspector

A person shall not be qualified for appointment as food inspector, unless he-

(1) Is a medical officer in charge of the health administration of a local area, or

(2) Is a graduate or a licentiate in medicine, and has received at least one month's training in food inspection and sampling work approved for the purpose by the Central or the State Government, or

(3) Is a qualified Sanitary Inspector having an experience as such for a minimum period of one year and has received at least 45 days training in food inspection and sampling

work under the Food (Health) Authority approved for the purpose by the Central Government, or

(4) Is a graduate in Science with Chemistry as one of the subjects, or a Graduate in Pharmacy or a graduate in Agriculture, Food Technology or Dairy Technology, and has received at least forty five days training in food inspection and sampling under the Food (Health) Authority approved for the purpose by the Central Government, or

(5) The period of training referred to in clauses [iii] and [iv] shall be extended to three months whenever considered necessary by the concerned Food (Health) Authority:

Provided that a person who is a food inspector on the date of commencement of the Prevention of Food Adulteration (Amendment) Rules, 1968, may continue to hold office as such subject to the terms and conditions of service applicable to him even though he does not fulfil the qualifications laid down in clauses [i] to [iv]

Duties of a Food Inspector

Following shall be the duty of the food inspector:

(1) To inspect as frequently as may be prescribed by the Food (Health) Authority or the local authority all establishments licensed for the manufacturer, storage or sale of an article of food within the area assigned to him;

(2) To satisfy himself that the conditions of the licences are being observed;

(3) To procure and send for analysis, if necessary, samples of any articles of food which he has reason to suspect are being manufactured, stocked or sold or exhibited for sale in contravention of the provisions of the Act or rules there under;

(4) To investigate any complaint which may be made to him in writing in respect of any contravention of the provision of the Act, or rules framed thereunder;

(5) To maintain a record of all inspections made and action taken by him in the performance of his duties, including the taking of the samples and the seizure of stocks, and to submit copies of such record to the health officer or the Food (Health) Authority as directed in this behalf;

(6) To make such enquiries and inspections as may be necessary to detect the manufacturer, storage or sale or articles of food in contravention of the Act or rules framed there under;

(7) To stop any vehicle suspected any food intended for sale or delivery for human consumption;

(8) When so authorized by the health officer, having jurisdiction in the local area concerned or the Food (Health) Authority, to detain imported packaged which he has reason to suspect contain food, the import or sale of which is prohibited;

(9) To perform such other duties as may be entrusted to him by the health officer having jurisdiction in the local area concerned or the Food (Health) Authority;

Local (Health) Authority to send Report to Person Concerned

The (Health) Authority shall immediately after the institutions of prosecution forward a copy of the report of the result of analysis in Form III delivered to him under sub-rule (3) of Rule 7, by registered post or by hand, as may be appropriate, to the person from whom the sample of the article was taken by the Food Inspector, and simultaneously also to the person, if any, whose name; address and other particulars have been disclosed under Section 14A of the Act:

Provided that where the sample conforms to the prcvisions of the Act or the rules made thereunder, and no prosecution is intended under sub-section (2), or no action is intended under sub-section (2-E) of Section 13 of the Act, the Local (Health)

Authority shall intimate the result to the Vendor from whom the sample has been taken and also to the person, whose name, address and other particulars have been disclosed under Section 14A of the Act, within 10 days from the receipt of the report from the Public Analyst.

Forms of Order not to Dispose of Stock and of Bond

Where the food inspector keeps any article of food in the safe custody of the vendor under sub-section (4) of Section 10-

(1) He shall, after sealing such article of food, make an order to the vendor in Form IV (Ref Fig. 21B) and the vendor shall comply with such an order, and

FORM IV
(See Rule 10)

To

(Name and address of the vendor)

....

....

....

Whereas * ....
intended for food which is in your possession appears to me to be adulterated/misbranded:

Now therefore under sub-section (4) of Section 10 of the Prevention of Food Adulteration Act, 1954 (37 of 1945). I hereby direct you to keep in your safe custody the said sealed stock subject to such orders as may be issued subsequently in relation thereto.

Food Inspector
Area...........

Place:
Date:

Figure 21B: Specimen of Form IV

(2) He may require the vendor to execute a bond in Form IV-A (Ref. Fig. 21C).

FORM IV-A
(See Rule 10)
BOND OF SURETY

Know all men by these presents that we (i)........................ .... Son of .... resident of .... and (ii) .... parteners of Messrs .... hereinafter called the Vendor(s) and (iii) .... son of .... resident of .... hereinafter called the Vendor(s) and (iv)................................. son of resident of .... hereinafter called the surety/sureties are held and firmly borne unto the President of India/Governor of..........hereinafter called the Government in the sum of.........Rupees to be paid to the Government, for which payment will and truly to be made. We firmly bind ourselves jointly and severally by these presents.

Signed this.........day of..........................on thousand nine hundred and .... Whereas Shri .... Food Inspector has seized............................(Here, insert the description of materials together with number/quantity and total price) hereinafter referred to as the said article, from .... (specify the place);

And whereas on the request of the Vendor(s) the Government agreed to keep the said article in the safe custody of the Vendor(s) on the condition of the Vendor(s) executing a bond in the terms hereinafter contained and supported by surety/two sureties which the Vendor(s) has/have agreed to do .... Now the condition of the above written obligation is such that if in the event of the Vendor(s) failure to produce infact the said article before such court or Authority and on such date (s) as may be specified by the said Food Inspector from time to time the Vendor(s) and/or the surety/sureties forthwith pay to the Government on demand and without a demur sum of .... rupees the said bond will be void and of no effect. Otherwise the same shall be and remain in full force and virtue.

(contd...)

These presents further witness as follows:

(i) The liability of the surety/sureties hereunder shall not be impaired or discharged by reason of time being granted by or any forbearance, act or omission of the Government whether with or without the knowledge or consent of the sureties or either of them in respect of or in relation to all or any of the obligations or condition to be performed or discharged by Vendor(s). Nor shall it be necessary for the Government to she the Vendor(s) before suing the sureties or either of them for the amount due hereunder;

(ii) This bond is given under the Prevention of Food Adulteration Act, 1954 for the performance of an act in which the public are interested.

(iii) The Government shall bear the stamp duty payable on these presents.

In witness whereof these presents have been signed by the Vendor(s) and the surety/sureties the day herein above mentioned by Shri .... on behalf of the President of India on the date ....

Witnesses:

I,.........................,..............(Signature)

(Name and address)...............

...............................(Signature)

(Name and address)...............

...............................(Signature)

Signature________________ (Vendor)

Signature________________ (Vendor)

Signature________________ (Surety)

Signature________________ (Surety)

for and on behalf of the President of India/Governor of________________

Signature________________

(Name and designation________

____

Figure 21C : Specimen of Form IVA: Bond of Surety

Form of Receipt for Food Seized by a Food Inspector

For every article of food seized and carried away by food inspector under sub-section (4) of Section 10 of the Act, a receipt in Form V (Ref Fig. 21D) shall be given by the inspector to the person from whom the article was seized.

Notice of Intention to take Sample for Analysis

When a Food Inspector takes a sample of an article for the purpose of analysis, he shall give notice of his intention to do

FORM V
(See Rule II)

To

(Name and address of the Vendor)

....

....

....

The stock of articles of food detailed below has this day been seized by me under the provision of sub-section (4) of Section 10 Invoice No .... Place .... of the Prevention of Food Adulteration Act, 1954 (37 of 1954), from the premises of .... Situated at ....

Details of articles of food seized.

Food Inspector

Area............

Place:

Date:

Figure 21D: Specimen of Form V

FORM VI
(See Rule 12)

To

....

....

I have this day taken from the premises of .... situated at .... samples of the food specified below to have the same analyzed by the public analyst for...

Details of food

Food Inspector

Area...........

Place:

Date:

Figure 21E: Specimen of Form VI

so in writing in Form VI (Ref Fig. 21E) then and there, to the person from whom he takes the sample and simultaneously, by appropriate means, also to the persons if any, whose name, address and other particulars have been disclosed under Section 14-A of the Act.

Provided that in case where a food inspector draws a sample from an open container, he shall also draw a sample from the container in original condition of the same article bearing the same declaration if such container is available, and intimate this fact to the Public Analyst.

POWERS OF FOOD INSPECTORS

(1) A Food Inspector shall have power-

(a) To take samples of any article of food from-

(i) Any person selling such article;

(ii) Any person who is in the course of conveying, delivering or preparing to deliver such article to a purchaser or consignee;

(iii) A consignee after delivery of any such article to him; and

(b) To send such sample for analysis to the public analyst for the local area within which such sample has been taken;

(c) With the previous approval of the Local (Health) Authority having jurisdiction in the local are concerned, or with the previous approval of the food (Health) Authority, to prohibit the sale of and article of food in the interest of public health.

For the purposes of sub-clause (iii) of clause (a), "consignee" does not include a person who purchases or receives any article of food for his own consumption.

(2) Any Food Inspector may enter and inspect any place where any article of food is manufactured, or stored for sale, or stored for the manufacturer of any other article of food for sale, or exposed or exhibited for sale or where any adulterant is manufactured or kept and take samples of such article of food or adulterant for analysis:

No sample of any article of food, being primary food, shall be taken under this sub-section if it is not intended for sale as such food.

(3) Where any sample is taken under clause (a) of sub-section (1) or sub-section (2), its cost calculated at the rate at which the article is usually sold to the public shall be paid to the person from whom it is taken.

(4) If any article intended for food appears to any food inspector to be adulterated or misbranded, he may seize and carry away or keep in the safe custody of the vendor such article in order that it may be dealt with as hereinafter provided and he shall, in either case, take a sample of such article and submit the same for analysis to Public Analyst:

Where the food inspector keeps such article in the safe custody of the vendor he may require the vendor to execute a bond for a sum of money equal to the value of such article with one or more sureties as the food inspector deems fit and the vendor shall execute the bond accordingly.

Where any article of food seized under sub-section (4) is of a perishable nature and the Local (Health) Authority is satisfied that such article of food is so deteriorated that it is unfit for human consumption, the said Authority may, after giving notice in writing to the vendor, cause the same to be destroyed.

(5) The power conferred by this section includes power to break open any package in which any article of food may be contained or to break open the door of any premises where any article of food may be kept for sale:

The power to break open the package or door shall be exercised only after the owner or any other person in charge of the package or, as the case may be, in occupation of the premises if he is present therein, refuses to open the package or door on being called upon to do so, and in either case after recording the reasons for doing so:

The food inspector shall, in exercising the powers of entry upon, and inspection of any place under this section follow, as far as may be, the provisions of the Code and Criminal Procedure, 1973 (2 of 1974) relating to the search or inspection of a place by a police officer executing a search warrant issued under that Code.

(6) Any adulterant found in the possession of a manufacturer or distributor of, or dealer in, any article of food or in any of the premises occupied by him as such and for the possession of which he is unable to account to the satisfaction of the Food Inspector, and any books of account or other documents found in his possession or control and which would be useful for, or relevant to, any investigation or proceeding under this Act may be seized by the Food Inspector and a sample of such adulterant submitted for analysis to a public analyst:

No such books of account or other document shall be seized by the Food Inspector except with the previous approval of the authority to which he is officially subordinate.

(7) Where the Food Inspector takes any action under clause (a) of sub-section (1), sub-section (2), sub-section (4), or sub-section (6), he shall, call one or more persons to be present at the time when such action is taken and take his or their signatures.

Where any books of account or other documents are seized under sub-section (6), the Food Inspector shall, within a period not exceeding thirty days from the date of seizure, return the same to the person from whom they were seized after copies there of extracts therefrom as certified by that person in such manner as may be prescribed have been taken;

Where such person refuses to so certify, and a prosecution has been instituted against him under this Act, such books of account or other documents shall be returned to him only after copies there of or extracts there from as certified by court have been taken.

When any adulterant is seized under sub-section (6), the burden of proving that such adulterant is not meant for purpose of adulteration shall be on the person from whose possession such adulterant was seized.

(8) Any Food Inspector may exercise the powers of a police officer under section 42 of the Code of Criminal

Procedure, 1973 (2 of 1974) for the purpose of ascertaining the true name and residence of the person from whom a sample is taken or an article food is seized.

(9) Any Food Inspector exercising powers under this Act or under the rules made thereunder who-

(a) vexatiously and without any reasonable grounds of suspicion seizes any article of food or adulterant; of

(b) commits any other act to the injury of any person without having reason to believe that such act is necessary for the execution of his duty; shall be guilty of an offence under this Act, and shall be punishable for such offence with fine which shall not be less than five hundred rupees but which may extend to one thousand rupees.

Power vested in the Food Inspector is not arbitrary. As the standard of Food is prescribed by Rules, it is only the Rules that can be impeached.

GENERAL POWER OF THE FOOD INSPECTORS

(1) Though section 10 is headed as "Powers of the Food Inspectors" its subsections do not deal only with the powers of a Food Inspectors, some deal with his powers and some with his duties. A vendor can be punished for preventing an Inspector from exercising his powers under the Act but cannot be punished for preventing him from doing duties.

(2) The Act is a social piece of legislation meant to control and curb adulteration of articles of food and being in the interest of public health it has to liberally construed and no limitation can be inferred on the powers of the Food Inspector whose primary duty is to see that the adulterated articles are neither manufactured nor stored nor sold.

(3) Suppose a particular state government does not choose to frame any Rules at all under the provisions of the Parent Act namely the Prevention of Food Adulteration Act, 1954, can it be argued with any show of force that in such cases the Food Inspector would become absolutely powerless and wholly ineffective? The answer must be in the negative because it is manifest that the duties and functions of the Food Inspector spring from the parent statute and are not in any way co-related to the additional duties provided for in the Rules which may be framed by the State Government.

The Food Inspector can take Samples of Food only under Certain Conditions

(1) Under section 10 the Food Inspector is authorized to take samples of food only from particular persons indulging in a specified course of business activity. The immediate or ultimate end of such activity is the sale of an article of food. The persons from whom the Food Inspector can take samples are either seller or conveyor or deliverer, manufacturer, consignee or storer.

Moreover, the article of food must be one which is "manufactured", "stored" or "exposed for sale". It follows that if an article of food is not intended for sale and is in the possession of a person who does not fulfill the character of a seller, conveyor, deliverer, consignee, manufacturers or storer for sale such as one referred to in sub-section (1) (a) and (2) of section 10, the Food Inspector will not be competent under the law to take the sample.

(2) Adulterated Food though not food for human consumption, sample of it can be taken for analysis.

(3) Section 10 cannot be so construed as to deprive the seller of his defence under section 19(2).

(4) It is not obligatory on the part of the Food Inspector to seize the entire stock in shop at the time of purchasing the article for the purpose of analysis.

(5) Section 10 does not create obligation on person mentioned therein to actively cooperate with the Food Inspector in taking sample by handing it over to him.

(6) Demand by the Food Inspector to give sample of article sold-Refusal by person selling article to give such sample even if act is valid. On surety's failure to produce the accused before the Magistrate, the Magistrate has jurisdiction to forfeit such bond.

(7) The Food Inspector is not a Police Officer for the purpose of Section 25 of the Evidence Act.

PROCEDURE TO BE FOLLOWED BY FOOD INSPECTORS

(1) When a Food Inspector takes a sample of food for analysis, he shall-

(a) Give notice in writing then and there of his intention to have it so analysed to the person from whom he has taken the sample and to the person, if any, whose name, address and other particulars have been disclosed under section 14-A;

(b) Except in special cases provided by rules under this Act, divide the sample then and there into three parts and mark and seal or fasten up each part in such a manner as its nature permits and take the signature or thumb impression of the person from whom the sample has been taken in such place and in such manner as may be prescribed:

Provided that where such person refuses to sign or put his thumb-impression and Food Inspector shall call upon one or more witnesses and take his or their signatures or thumb-impressions, as the case may be, in lieu of the signature or thumb-impression of such person;

(c) (i) Send one of the parts for-analysis to the public analyst under intimation to the Local (Health) Authority and (ii)

Send the remaining two parts to the Local (Health) Authority for the purposes of sub-section (2) of this section and sub-section (2-A and 2-E) of section 13.

(2) Where the part of the sample sent to the public analyst under sub-clause (i) of clause (c) of sub-section (1) is lost or damaged the Local (Health) Authority shall, on a requisition made to it by the public analyst or the Food Inspector dispatch one of the parts of the sample sent to it under sub-clause (ii) of the said clause (c) to the public analyst for analysis.

(3) When a sample of any article of food or adulterant is taken under sub-section (1) or sub-section (2) of section 10 the Food Inspector shall, by the immediately succeeding working day, send a sample of the article of food or adulterant or both, as the case may sample of the article of food or adulterant or both, as the case may be, in accordance with the rules prescribed for sampling to the public analyst for the local area concerned.

(4) An article of food seized under sub-section (4) of section 10, unless destroyed under sub-section (4-A) of the section, and any adulterant seized under sub-section (6) of that section shall be produced before a magistrate as soon as possible and in any case not later than seven days after the receipt of the report of the public analyst:

Provided that if any application is made to the magistrate in this behalf by the person from whom any article of food has been seized, the magistrate shall by order in writing direct the Food Inspector to produce such article before him within such time as may be specified in the order.

(5) If it appears to the magistrate on taking such evidence as he may deem necessary-

(a) That the article of food produced before him under sub-section (4) is adulterated or misbranded, he may order it-

(i) To be forfeited to the Central government, the State Government or the local authority, as the case may be; or

(ii) To be destroyed at the cost of the owner or the person from whom it was seized so as to prevent it being used as human food; or

(iii) To be so disposed of as to prevent its being again exposed for sale or used for food under its deceptive name; or

(iv) To be returned to the owner, on his executing a bond with or without sureties, for being sold under its appropriate name or, where the magistrate is satisfied that the article a food is capable of being made to conform to prescribed standards for human consumption after reprocessing, for being sold after reprocessing, for being sold after reprocessing under the supervision of such officer as may be specified in the order;

(b) That the adulterant seized under sub-section (6) of section 10 and produced before him is apparently of a kind which may be employed for purposes of adulteration and for the possession of which the manufacturer distributor or dealer as the case may be, is unable to account satisfactorily he may order it to be forfeited to the Central Government the State Government or the local authority as the case may be.

(6) If it appears to the magistrate that any such-

(a) Article of a food is not adulterated; or

(b) Adulterant which is purported to be an adulterant is not an adulterant,

The person from whose possession the article of food or adulterant was taken shall be entitled to have it restored to him and it shall be in the discretion of the magistrate to award such person from such fund as the State Government may direct in this behalf, such compensation not exceeding the actual loss which he has sustained as the magistrate may think proper.

Purchaser may have Food Analysed

Nothing contained in this Act shall be held to prevent a purchaser of any article of food other then a Food Inspector from having such article analysed by the Public Analyst on payment of such fees as may be prescribed and from receiving from the Public Analyst a report of his analysis;

Provided that such purchaser shall inform the vendor at the time of purchase of his intention to have such article so analysed:

Provided further that the provisions of sub-section (1) sub-section (2) and sub-section (3) of section 11 shall, as far as may be, apply to a purchaser of article of food who intends to have such article so analysed, as they apply to a Food Inspector who takes a sample of Food for Analysis:

Provided also that if the report of the Public Analyst shows that the article of food is adulterated, the purchaser shall be entitled to get refund of the fees paid by him under this section.

CHAPTER 22

SAMPLES: Sealing, Fastening and Despatch

Samples of food for the purpose of analysis shall be taken in clean dry bottles or jars or in order suitable containers which shall be closed sufficiently tight to prevent leakage, evaporation, or in case of dry substance, entrance of moisture and shall be carefully sealed.

Rule 14 enjoins the Food Inspector to put the sample in clean dry bottles and to properly cork them so that there is no leakage or evaporation. The sample bottle produced in the court was found leaking. For non-compliance of Rule 14 the accused could not be convicted.

The Food Inspector did not produce any independent be hardly fair to discredit the report of the Public Analyst on a more suggestion of the accused of more theoretical possibility of tempering with the sample.

BOTTLES OR CONTAINERS TO BE LABELED AND ADDRESSED

All bottles or jars or other containers containing samples for analysis shall be properly labeled and the parcels shall be properly addressed. The label on any sample of food sent for analysis shall bear:

(1) Serial No.;

(2) Name of the sender with official designation, if any;

(3) Name of the vendor;

(4) Date and place of collection;

(5) Nature of article submitted for analysis;

(6) Nature and quantity of preservative, if any, added to the sample.

In the case of a sample of food which has been taken from Agmark sealed container, the label shall bear the following additional information:-

(1) Grade;

(2) Agmark label No./Batch No.;

(3) Name of packing station

MANNER OF PACKING AND SEALING THE SAMPLES

All samples of food sent for analysis shall be packed, fastened and sealed in the following manner, namely:-

(1) The stopper shall first be securely fastened so as to prevent leakage of the contents in transit;

(2) The bottle, jar or other container shall then be completely wrapped in fairly strong thick paper. The ends of the paper shall be neatly folded in and affixed by means of gum or other adhesive;

(3) A paper slip of the size that goes round completely from the bottom to top of the container, bearing the signature and code and serial number of the Local (Health) Authority, shall be pasted on the wrapper, the signature or the thumb impression of the person from whom the sample has been taken being affixed in such a manner that the paper slip and the wrapper both carry a part of the signature or thumb impression:

In case, the person, from whom the sample has been taken refuses to affix his signature or thumb impression, the signature or thumb impression of the witness shall be taken in the same manner;

(4) The proper cover shall be further secured by means of strong twine of thread both above and across the bottle, jar or other container, and the twine or thread shall then be fastened on the paper cover by means of sealing wax on which there shall be at least four distinct and clear impressions of the seal of the sender, of which one shall be at the top of the packet; one at the bottom and the other two on the body of the packet. The knots of the twine or thread shall be covered by means of sealing wax bearing the impression of the seal of the sender.

MANNER OF DISPATCHING CONTAINERS OF SAMPLES

The containers of the samples shall be dispatched in the following manner, namely:

(1) The sealed container of one part of the sample for analysis and a memorandum in Form VII (Ref Fig. 21A)shall be sent in a sealed packet to the public analyst immediately but not later than the succeeding working day by any suitable means.

(2) The sealed containers of the remaining two parts of the sample and two copies of the memoranda in Form VII (Ref Fig. 22A) shall be sent in a sealed packed to the Local (Health) Authority immediately but not later than the succeeding working day by day suitable means:

In the case of a sample of food which has been taken from container beating Agmark seal, the memorandum in Form VII shall contain the following additional information, namely:

(1) Grade;

(2) Agmark label No./Batch No.

(3) Name of packing station.

MEMORANDUM AND IMPRESSION OF SEAL TO BE SENT SEPARATELY

A copy of the memorandum and a specimen impression of the seal used to seal the packet shall be sent to the public analyst separately by registered post or delivered to him or to any person authorities by him.

Form VII
(See Rule 17)
MEMORANDUM OF PUBLIC ANALYST

The Public Analyst,

....

....

No.................................. Date the .... 200 ......
....Memorandum

The sample described below is sent herewith for analysis under claused (b) of sub-section (1) of section 10 and/or clause (c)(ii) of sub-section (1) of section 11 of the Prevention of Food Adulteration Act, 1954.

1. Serial No. of the sample. 2. Name of the vendor. 3. Date and place of collection. 4. Nature of article submitted for analysis. 5. Nature and quatity of perspective, if any, added to the sample.

2. A copy of this memo, and specimen impression of the seal used to seal the packet of sample is being sent separately by post/hand.

Food Inspector

Area.............

Figure 22A: Memorandum of Public Analyst: Form VII

ADDITION OF PRESERVATIVE TO SAMPLES

Any person taking a sample of any food for the purpose of analysis under the Act may add a preservative as may be prescribed from time to time to the sample for the purpose of maintaining it in a condition suitable for analysis.

Where the cover containing the seated packet of the sample for analysis enclosed together with a memorandum in Form VII was sent along with another packet containing the memorandum and specimen of the seal through the same peon, there was no infraction of Rule 18. As long as the copy of the memorandum that was required to be sent under Rule 18 was not sent together in the sense that all articles were not to be in the same packet or the same cover as article referred to in Rule 17 and the memorandum which was required to be sent under Rule 18 was sent independently in different cover, notwithstanding the fact that both are taken to the Analyst by the same peon, they must be said to have been sent independently of each other. The mere fact that the two packets were carried by the same peon would not mean that the material articles, namely, the samples and the memorandum on the one hand and the copy of the memorandum on the other hand are sent together. It is, therefore, permissible even under Rule 18 to send through the same person the memorandum of the specimen impression of the seal used to seal the packet but the memorandum and the specimen impression of the seal must be contained in two separate packets. They may be carried by the same person but should not be mixed together in the same packet.

Only says, "may add". The object of this rule is to maintain the preserve the sample in a good and suitable condition for analysis.

Rule 19 and 20 have to be read together. Rule 19 speaks about addition of preservative to the samples. It is significant to note that this rule only uses the words "May add preservative" as may be prescribed to be used in the case of samples of any milk and the proportions in which the same has to be used to the samples have been stated.

QUANTITY OF PRESERVATIVE TO BE ADDED

When Rule 20 prescribes two drops it provides for a fairly high degree of immunity and what is expected is that the rate be substantially complied with. No doubt where the rule is not in terms complied with and the prosecution relies on the substantial compliance, the persecution must prove that the compliance is substantial and has not affected the sample.

In so far as the preservative prescribed under Rule 20 is concerned, the object of adding that preservative is laid down in Rule 19 and that object is to maintain the sample in a condition suitable for analysis. It is with reference to that object that the adequacy of the preservative has to be considered. When the Rule speaks of formalin as a liquid containing a about 40 per cent formaldehyde in a aqueous solution, it indicates that the percentage of formaldehyde is not required to be precisely 40 per cent, but may be near about it and the preservative could nevertheless be under the Rule a good preservative.

PRESERVATIVE IN RESPECT OF MILK, CREAM, *DAHI*, *KHOA* AND GUR

The preservative used in the case of samples of any milk (including toned, separated and skimmed milk) standardized milk channa, skimmed milk chhanna, cream, mixed ice-cream, cream, ice candy, dahi, khoa and gur in liquid or semi-liquid form shall be the liquid commonly known as "formalin" that is to say, a liquid containing about 40 per cent of formaldehyde in aqueous solution in the proportion of 0.1 ml. (two drops) for 25 ml. Or 25 grams.

NATURE AND QUANTITY OF THE PRESERVATIVE TO BE NOTED ON THE LABEL

Whenever any preservative is added to a sample, the nature and quantity of the preservative added shall be clearly noted on the label to be affixed to the container.

QUANTITY OF SAMPLE TO BE SENT TO THE PUBLIC ANALYST

The quantity of sample of food to be sent to the*Public Analyst/Director for analysis shall be as specified as given in Table 22.1

Table 22.1: Quantity of Samples is to sent to the Public Analyst

Sl. No.	Article of food To be supplied	Approximate quantity
1.	Milk	220 ml.
2.	Ghee	150 grams
3.	Butter	150 grams
4.	*Khoa*	250 grams
5.	*Dahi*	200 grams
6.	Edible oils	125 grams
7.	Edible fats	125 grams
8.	Tea	125 grams
9.	*Atta*	200 grams
10.	Wheat flour	200 grams
11.	*Gur*	200 grams
12.	Cane sugar	200 grams
13.	Honey	250 grams
14.	Prepared food	500 grams
15.	Carbonated water	600 ml.
16.	Vanaspati	500 grams
17.	Species	150 grams
18.	Fruit and vegetable products, jams, jellies and the like	300 grams
19.	Pulses, cereals and the like	250 grams

(contd...)

Sl. No.	Article of food To be supplied	Approximate quantity
20.	(1) Asafoetida	100 grams
	(2) Compounded Asafoetida	200 grams
21.	Saffron	15 grams
22.	Ice cream and mixed ice cream	300 grams
22A	Silver leaf (Food grade)	1 grams
23.	Bread, toasts	500 grams
24.	Biscuits, cakes, pastries and allied products	500 grams
25.	Toffee, chocolate, hard boiled sugar confectionery and allied articles of food	300 grams
26.	Custard Powder	250 grams
27.	Cornflakes	200 grams
28.	Baby food	450 grams
29.	Prepared tea for saccharine and colour	250 ml. (grams)
30.	*Besan* (gram powder)	200 grams
31.	Cream	250 grams
32.	Dried Milk	252 grams
33.	Condensed milk	250 grams
34.	Curry powder	300 grams
35.	Cheese	200 grams
36.	Syrup	252 grams
37.	Foods (not specified)	200 grams

The object of Rule 22 of the Rules is that the Public Analyst should have sufficient quantity of the sample for analysis. The Public Analyst did not find any defect in the sample on account of its being less than the required quantity. The mere words 'approximate quantity to be supplied' in rule 22 of the Rules show that the requirement is directory and not mandatory in character. What is required is substantial and not strict compliance with the provision of this rule.

Contents of one or more similar sealed containers having identical labels to constitute the quantity of a food sample – Rule 22-A

Where food is sold or stocked for sale or for distribution in sealed containers having identical label declaration, the contents of one or more of such containers as may be required to satisfy the quantity prescribed in Rule 22 shall be treated to be a part of the sample.

MODEL QUESTIONS FOR EXAMINATIONS

OBJECTIVE TYPE QUESTIONS

1. State whether the following statements are 'True' (✔) or 'False' (×)

   (a) The Central Government appoints a Controller for hotel and lodging business ( )

   (b) Adulteration of food is not an offence, if it is not injurious to health. ( )

   (c) Central Food Laboratory is situated only in New Delhi. ( )

   (d) Analysis of food sample is done by Food Inspector. ( )

2. The following incident occurred at a restaurant:

   (a) Ms C became ill after ordering and drinking a bottle of lemonsoda. The bottle in fact contained caustic soda, which had been filled by an outside engineer Mr. X, when he called to clean the same equipment; he had emptied the bottle of lemonsoda, crossed out the word 'Lemonsoda' and substituted the word 'cleaner'. He had explained this and the cleaning method to the owner, Mr. BB who was deaf but tried to hide the fact from strangers, by nodding his agreement to everything.

(b) An inspection of the premises revealed a batch of mouldy pies in the fridge and working surfaces heavily impregnated with dirt.

(c) The menu offers "steak and kidney sudding." In fact the pudding was made with meat substitutes. Explain to Mr. B.B. his legal liability towards and the defences which he may put forward against:

1. MS C in the 1st case, and
2. the local authorities in all cases.

3 Has an offence, or have offences, been committed in the following situation? Give reasons for your answers referring to decided cases, where possible.

(a) A whole sale meat firm, A & Co, delivered some meat at a school, whilst a food inspector was looking over the Kitchen. The latter examined a cut of meat, which was described as 'Shoulder of lamb'. He identified it has being the fore quarters of a sheep, but not simply shoulder. Detailed inspections revealed that the meat was shoulder, breast and scrag end.

(b) The Negi's Café sole some cream cakes on 14th August as part of a high tea which they provided. One of the cake was mouldly and the cream in all of them was sour. Investigation revealed that the cakes had been made on June 30, and should have be eaten by August 9.

(c) 'B' delivered 50 plucked chickens at a hotel. The birds were uncovered and were stacked on the floor of a truck which was covered in mud and cow-dung. When challenged he claimed that he was carrying on an agricultural activity, not running a food business.

SHORT ANSWER QUESTIONS

1. Differentiate between:
   - (a) Public Analyst and Central Food Laboratory
   - (b) Central Committee for Food Standards and Central Food Laboratory.
2. How do local authorities enforce the Prevention of Food Adulteration Act (PFA Act) and its dependent regulation.
3. Explain the following and state the provision of PFA Act as regards to each one of them:
   - (a) Cereals
   - (b) Foodgrains
   - (c) Vinegar
   - (d) Gelatin
   - (e) Sweets and confectionery
   - (f) Food colours
   - (g) Silver leap
   - (h) Groundnut kernel.
4. Explain the provisions of PFA Act as regards to:
   - (a) Baking power
   - (b) Starchy foods
   - (c) Asafoetida
   - (d) Spices and condiments
   - (e) Beans
   - (f) Sweetening agents.

5. Write notes on:
   (a) Coffee
   (b) Edible fat
   (c) Milk and Milk products
   (d) Mangarine
   (e) Tea
   (f) Edible salt
   (g) Fruit products
   (h) Edible oils.
6. Explain the following:
   (a) Central Food Laboratory
   (b) Food
   (c) Local authority
   (d) Unwholesome and noxious food.
7. Write notes on:
   (a) Report of Public Analyst
   (b) Certificate of test a Analyst by CFL.
8. Write notes on:
   (a) Warranty
   (b) Offences
   (c) Punishments.
9. Explain the provisions of PFA Act regarding the labelling of the following items:
   (a) Fluid milk
   (b) Ice cream
   (c) Masala
   (d) Maida.

DESCRIPTIVE TYPE QUESTIONS

1. Explain the provisions of PFA Act as regards to conditions for sale and licence.
2. Define the term 'preservative and poisonous metals' classify the preservative and use of preservation in food.
3. Define emulsifying and stabilizing agents.
4. Explain the term:
   (i) Flavouring agents
   (ii) Insecticides and pesticides
   (iii) Solvent extorted oil and edible oil.
5. Define the term 'food poisoning'. Explain the provision of the PFA Act, as regards to food poisoning and the penalties imposed for such offences.
6. Explain the main objectives of the Prevention of Food Adulteration Act and describe the significance of the provisions of the law in the present-day scenario.
7. Explain under what circumstances an article of food shall be deemed to be adulterated.
8. Define 'misbranded food'. Explain the cases under which an article of food shall be deemed to be misbranded.
9. Explain the procedure for constitution of Central of Committee for Food Standards.
10. What is the objective of the Central Food Laboratory? Name the Central Food Laboratories and their specified areas.
11. What is analysis of food? Explain the whole procedure for analysis of food as per Prevention of Food Adulteration Act.

12. Explain the general provisions as to food standards. Give some examples.
13. Differentiate between Public Analyst and Food Inspector. State the qualification required for a Public Analyst.
14. Give an account of the duties of public analyst.
15. Define the terms 'Food Inspector'. State the qualificationx and duties of a Food Inspector.
16. Explain the duties and powers of Food Inspector under the Prevention of Food Adulteration Act.
17. Explain the procedure to be followed by Food Inspector while taking sample of food for analysis.
18. Define the term 'warranty' and explain the form of warranty.
19. Explain the provisions of FPA Act as regards to colouring matter.
20. Describe the provisions as regards to contents of lebelling of food. Explain with examples.
21. Explain the provisions and regulations of sales as per PFA Act.

FREQUENTLY ASKED QUESTION WITH ANSWER

1. **What is Food?**

   'Food' means any article used as Food or drink for human consumption other than drugs and water.

2. **What is adulterated food?**

   Detailed definition is given under Section (2) or the PFA Act, 1954. But in general, if anything is added or taken-out from the food which adversely affects the quality of the food article, may be treated as adulterated food.

3. **What is mis-branded food?**

   The term has been described under section (2) (ix) of the PFA Act 1954. But in general, mis-braining means false claims or something wrong or against the provisions of the PFA Act in the labelling of the food article.

4. **In cases any good article is suspected to be adulterated, what to do?**

   Complaint may be made to the Officers as mentioned in the Act.

5. **What action will be taken on the complaints?**

   A team of Food Inspector under the supervision of SDMs shall lift the samples of food articles as per procedure laid down under the PFA Act an the samples will be sent for analysis to the Public Analyst, who will deliver the report within 40 days.

6. **In case, if sample is found adulerated, what action is taken?**

   The persons responsible for adulteration are identified by the investigating Food Inspects and Prosecution is launched after examining the matter by the Legal experts and the Director (PFA).

7. **Where the Prosecution cases are launched?**

There is a special designed Court to deal with the fine of Rs. 1,000/- which may be extended upto life imprisonment with the fine depending upto the gravity of the offence.

8. **What is the penal the adulterators?**

Minimum 6 months imprisonment with the fine of Rs 1,000/- which may be extended upto life imprisonment with the fine depending upto the gravity of the offence.

9. **If any person wants to get a sample analyses, what is to be done?**

Take sufficient guality of the sample and contact the Public Analyst at Department of Prevention of food Adulteration; of the concern area with the prescribed analysis fee. The sample may be analyses after due course of time.

10. **Who can start the business of food articles?**

Any person can do the business of food articles but he has to abide by the provisions of the PFA Act & Rules.

INDEX

A

Adulterated article of food 7, 208
Ajowan (Bishop's Weed) 66
Almond oil 95
Amaranth 120
Ammonium compounds 108
Amomum subulatum 52
Analysis of food samples 203, 218
Aniseed or *saunf* 66
Annatto 127
Anticaking agents 169
Anti-oxidants, emulsifying and stabilizing and Anti-baking agents 163-170
Appointment of Secretary and other Staff 216
Arrowroot 101
Artificial sweetener 179
Artificially coloured 136
Asafoetida (*hing* or *hingra*) 102
    compounded 148
Atta 74
    fortified 74
    protein Rich (paustik) 75

B

Bakery shortening 110
Baking powder 101
b-Carotene 122
Bean 67
Beef fat or suet 96
Besan 78
Bixa orecallana 127
Boiled milk 31
Bottles or containers to be labelled and addressed 265
Brassica alba 61
Brassica compestris 60
Bread-wheat-meal bread (brown bread) and white 85
Brown-phase reaction 124
Buffalo milk 32
Bura 105
Butter Toffee 114

C

Cane Sugar 104
Capsicum frutescens 53
Caramel 125
Caraway Black (*Carum bulbocastenum*) (*Siahjeera*) 50-51
Carbia callosa 179
Carbide gas 177
Carbohydrates 125
Carbonated water 17
Cardamom (*chhoti elachi*) 51-52
Cardamom amomum (*badi elachi*) 52-53
Carmoisine 130, 131
Carum bulbocastanum 51
Cash Memo, specimen of 202
Cassia bark 147

Cassia taj (whole) 55
Catechu (edible) 111
Central Committee for Food Standards 215
Central Food Laboratory 217, 218
Central Government
    power of the to make rules 196
Cereals 74
Certificate of Test or Analysis by the CFL 222
Cheese (hard) 37
Chhenna or *Paneer* 36
Chicory 48, 49
Chillies (*lal mirchi*) 53, 148
Chlorophyll 124
Cinnamon (*dalchini*) 54, 148
Cloves (*laung*) 55
Coal-tar 133, 149
Coal-tar Dyes 137
Cocoa butter 97, 98
Coconut oil (*naryal ka tel*) 88
Coffee 46 47
    blended with chicory 143
    chicory 49
    chicory mixture: form of labels 143
    French 49
    ground 48
Colour mixture 133
– preparation 133
– reaction 123
Colouring matter 136
Colours 139
    maximum limit of permitted 139
    sale of permitted food colours 180
Common salt 87
Condition for sale 182
Coriander (*dhania*) 55, 56
Cornflakes 81, 82
Cotton seed oil (*binola ka tel*) 88
Cream excluding sterilized cream 36
Cube Sugar 106
Cumin (*safed jeera*) 56
– black (*kalonji*) 57
Curry powder 65, 148
Custard powder 82
Custom laws and Powers of Customs Officers 228

D

Dahi or Curd 36
Damaged grain 80
Definition of anti-oxidant 163
Definition of emulsifying and stabilizing agents 168
Deshi (cooking) butter 43
Dextrose 106
Director of Central Food Laboratory 4, 8
Distance of surrounding line 141
Dry fruits and nuts: sale of insect-damaged 181
Duties of Public Analyst 231, 236

E

Edible fat 96
– oils 87, 88
Elettaria cardamomum 51
Emulsifying agents 168
Erythrosine 120, 121

F

Fast Red E 132
Fat spread 98
Fennel (*saunf*) 57, 58
Fenugreek (*methi*) 58
Flavouring agents, 152
Food (Health) Authority 9
– Adulteration Act 4

– colours 117
– grain 79, 80
– inspectors 230, 248
duties of 249
general power 208, 255 259
qualifications of 248
– is either adulterated or not 208
– Poisoning, Offences, Warranty, Punishment and 188
Foreign material 79
Forfeiture of property 194
Form of Receipt for Food Seized by a Food Inspector 254
– – warranty 204
– – warranty: specimen of Form VI-A 205
– – order not to dispose of stock and of bond 251
Fruit beverage 70
– chutney 72
– drinks 70
– juice 68
– products 68
– squash 69
– syrup 69

G

Gelatin 109, 111, 112
Ghee (Pure Clarified Fat) 44
– or butter: sale or use for sale of admixtures of 179
– standard of quality of 44
Ginger (*sonth*, *adrak*) 59
Goat fat 97
Golden syrup 107
Groundnut 149
– kernel 134
– oil (*moongh-phali-ka-tel*) 89
Gur or jaggery 105

H

Hingra 147
Honey dew 105, 179

I

Ice-candy or ice lollies or edible ices 105
Ice-Cream 38, 147
Icing sugar 107
Identification tests 124, 126
Imitations not to be Marked "Pure" 143
Indian Pharmacopoeia 108
Indigo carmine 121, 122
Inorganic matter and pigments 137
Insect 80
– damaged matter 51, 53
Insecticides 152, 153

J

Jam 71

K

Kali sarson (*Brassica compestris*) 60, 61
Kangra tea 47, 179
Khoya 42
Kulfi and chocolate ice-cream 38

L

Labels 141, 142
container of food which contains preservative 163
for proprietary or fancy trade names 142
labelling of foods 136, 139
languages of the particulars or declaration 141
not to contain false or misleading statements 141

not to contain reference to act or rules contradictory to required particulars 142
not to use words implying recommendations by medical profession 142
unauthorised use of words showing imitation prohibited, 142
Lard 97
Legislative history of Section 16(1) 209
Licence, conditions for 182, 183
Light black pepper 63, 147
Linseed oil (*tisi ka tel*) 90
Local (Health) Authority 10
– Area 9
– Authority 9
Low and High Fat Cocoa Powder 97
Lozenges 115

M

Macaroni products (Macaroni, spaghetti, vermicelli) 83
Mace (*jaepatri*) 60
Magistrate's Power to Impose Enhanced Penalties (S 195
Mahua Oil 89
Maida (wheat flour) 75, 76
protein rich (*paushtik*) 77
Maize (corn) oil 94
Malai 36
Manner of dispatching containers of samples 267
– – packing and sealing the samples 266
Manufacturers, distributors and dealers to give warranty 157
Maragarine 96
Marmalade 72
Matar dal 80
Milk 30
condensed milk or desiccated (dried) milk 144
– – sweetened 39
– – unsweetened (evaporated milk) 39
– skimmed milk sweetened 40
– – milk unsweetened 39
designation of 33
double toned milk 31, 32
flavoured milk 31
fluid Milk 146
ices or milk lollies 38
infant milk food 42
malted 150
– milk food 83
– toffee 114
mixed 31
partly skimmed milk powder (sour) 41, 42
pasteurization 30
powder 40
products 36
recombined milk 31, 32
sale of butter milk 227
should be stirred by the Public Analyst 240
skimmed milk 31, 32, 148
– – *chhenna* or skimmed milk *paneer* 37
– – powder 41
standardised 31
toned milk 31, 32
Misbranded Article of Food 10
Misri (palm and sugarcane) 104
Moisture 80
Monosodium 150
Mustard (*rai, sarson*) 60, 61
– oil (*sarson-ka-tel*) 90, 149, 228
– – containing some *til* oil 228

N

Niger seed oil (*sargiya ka tel*) 93
Nomination of Persons by a Company 207
Notes of addition, admixture or deficiency in food 150
Notice of Intention to take Sample for Analysis 254
Nutmeg (*jaiphal*) 62
Nutritional food 140

O

Object of severe punishment under the Act 211
Offences by companies 192
Olive Oil 91

P

Packaging 11, 136, 139
Palmolein149
Paneer 36
Pearl barley 78
Penalties 188
Pepper black (*kali mirch*) 62
Pesticides 152, 153
Pinheads 63
Poisonous metals 163
Ponceau 130
– 4R 129
Poppy (*khas-khas*) 63
– seed oil 91
Power of Court 195, 214
Premises 11
Preservatives
to samples 159, 269
classification of 159
in respect of milk, cream, *dahi*, *khoa* 270
nature and quantity of 270
poisonous metals and anti-oxidants 159
restricated in food articales 161
Prevention of adulteration of food and beverages 3
Primary article of food 12
Procedure to be Followed by Food Inspectors 261
Processed cheese 37
Prohibition and regulation of sales 173
– of manufacture, sale, etc. 229
– – use of carbide gas 176
Protection of action taken in good faith 196
Public Analyst 230, 240, 268
qualifications of 230
Purchase sample for analysis 232
Purchaser may have Food Analysed 264

Q

Quantity of preservative to be added 270
– – sample to be sent to the public analyst 271

R

Rapeseed oil (*toria* oil) 90, 149
Raw material 125
Refined Sugar 104
– vegetable oil 95
Repeal and saving 200
Report of Public Analyst 234, 238, 245
Requirements of fast Red E 132
Riboflavin 128
Roasted coffee 48
Rodent hair and excreta 80
Rolled oats (quick-cooking oats) 84

S

Saccharin sodium 108
Safflowers oil (*barrey ka tel*) 92
Saffron (*kesar*) 63
Sale of certain admixtures prohibited 173
– – food 12
Salt 87
Sealng
despatch 265-276
dispatching containers 267
fastening 265-276
memorandum and impression of seal 268
packing of 266-267
sample of an article of food 12
sealing of 266-267
Sauce 73
Saunf 66
Semoilan (*suji* or *rawa*) 77
Silver leap (*chandi ka warq*) 134
Solubility 123
Solvent extorted oils 156
extracted edible flour 156, 157
Soyabean oil 94
Spectrophotometric Requirement 123, 129
Spices and condiments 50
Stabilizing agents 168
Standards of quality of the various articles of foods 226
Starchy foods 101
State Government
power of the 9, 199
Sterilization 31
Sugar confectionery 113
Sunset yellow 119
Sweetening agents 104
Sweets and confectionery 113

T

Table (Creamery) Butter 43
Taramira oil 92
Tartrazine 117
Tea 46
Theobroma cocoa 97
Til oil (Gingelly or sesame oil) 92, 177
Toffee 114, 115
Tomato
juice 68
ketchup 70
relish 70
sauce 70
Turmeric (*haldi*) 64

U

Unwholesome and noxious food 12
Usable eating in foods 138
Use of caramel 136
– – Class II preservatives 160, 163
– – emulsifying and stabilizing 169
– – flesh of naturally dead animals 180
– – more than one Class II Preservative 160
– – poisonous metals 164
– – starch phosphate 169

V

Vanaspati 80, 109, 111
Vinegar 109, 111
synthetic 111

W

Warranty 201
Water-melon seed oil 95
Weighment of sample 240
Whole wheat barley powder 78

Z

Zingiber officinale 59